Date Due

ILLINOIS BIOLOGICAL
MONOGRAPHS

Vol. II   July, 1915   No. 1

———

PUBLISHED UNDER THE
AUSPICES OF THE GRADUATE SCHOOL BY
THE UNIVERSITY OF ILLINOIS

THE CLASSIFICATION OF LEPIDOPTEROUS LARVAE

WITH TEN PLATES

BY

STANLEY BLACK FRACKER

Contributions from the
Entomological Laboratories of the University of Illinois
No. 43.

THESIS

Submitted in Partial Fulfilment of the Requirements
for the Degree of Doctor of Philosophy in
Entomology in the Graduate School
of the University of Illinois
1914

TABLE OF CONTENTS

ACKNOWLEDGMENTS

The subject of this paper was suggested by Professor Alexander D. MacGillivray in the fall of 1912. During the two years since that time the writer has become more and more convinced of the necessity for and value of taxonomic studies of immature insects. While a classification based on larvae would doubtless include as serious mistakes as one in which only the adults were considered, combining the two methods results in the elimination of a great many errors. In addition to this purely scientific ideal, the demand of students and economic entomologists for some means of identifying larvae without rearing them has acted as an even stronger incentive to persistent effort.

The author wishes to express his sincere appreciation of the suggestions and criticisms of Professor MacGillivray throughout the preparation of the paper and of the inspiration which has come from association with him. The authorities of the University of Illinois have, through liberal appropriation, made possible the purchase of material from Dr. O. Staudinger and A. Bang-Haas of Dresden, from the Kny-Scheerer Company, from the Ward Natural Science Establishment, and from Mr. Wm. Beutenmüller. They have also enabled the writer to study for several months at the United States National Museum, where the series of lepidopterous larvae is probably the most extensive in the world. For securing this assistance, for continuous encouragement, and for placing at his disposal the material of the Illinois State Laboratory of Natural History, the author gives hearty thanks to Professor Stephen A. Forbes. Grateful acknowledgments are due Dr. L. O. Howard for his courtesy in granting use of the entomological collections of the National Museum. To Dr. Harrison G. Dyar, Mr. August Busck, and Mr. Carl Heinrich, the writer is indebted for numerous suggestions and for making these collections accessible and helpful.

PART ONE. THE HOMOLOGY OF THE SETAE

I. INTRODUCTION

One of the most serious difficulties in the path of scientific progress is the lack of a means of expression common to all the workers in a single field.   When a particular term means one thing to one scientist and something else to another, no amount of learning will make the opinions of these men intelligible to each other until they understand the differ- ence.   In human anatomy, the large number of workers, the excellent figures, and the antiquity and narrow limits of the subject have to a large extent removed this confusion but in other fields of biology the mistakes it causes are still apparent.   This is true in entomology and very noticeably so in the study of larvae.

The various systems of numerals which have been applied to the setal arrangement of lepidopterous larvae are all based on the simple plan of numbering the setae from the dorsomeson.   Except in the most conspicuous cases, little consideration is taken of the relations of the different segments to each other.   Several authors have already intro- duced confusion by applying the numbers in a slightly different way from that first suggested, but no careful investigation has been made of the real relations of the larval chaetotaxy of one group to that of another.

Realizing the conflicts in the application of the numerals now in use and the nature of the objections to them, the writer began the study of caterpillars with an investigation of the homology and homotypy of the setae.   The object of the former was a determination of the changes which have taken place in the ancestral history of any particular body segment, such as the prothorax, and the application of a given name to the same structure throughout the entire order.   The study of the latter, homotypy, was taken up for the purpose of finding the relation of the setal pattern of the different body segments to each other, in the hope of applying the same name to the same structure throughout the entire body.   All the segments behind, but not including, the head were studied and satisfactory results were obtained for all except the tenth or last abdominal segment.

It is intended that the figures, descriptions, and definitions shall make every statement in this paper absolutely definite and that they shall be so clear that a novice may be able to make a complete description of a caterpillar without the possibility of confusion as to his meaning. New species and new instars should be described in a manner which will make like specimens recognizable in the future without repeating the breeding. Such complete descriptions in the published records are very few at the present time.

HISTORICAL

The first worker to find and describe a primary plan of the setae of caterpillars was Wilhelm Müller (1886), in a paper on the Nymphalidae. After discussing the arrangement in the first stage of these butterfly larvae, he says: "We find in the first stage, on the abdomen of all forms considered, certain setae. Tho of many different forms their constant arrangement shows them to be homologous. We call these setae primary. * * Doubt as to the similarity between the mesothorax and metathorax and the abdomen seems to be out of the question." In an appendix, brief notes on the chaetotaxy of the larvae of other families of Lepidoptera are given. Careful comparison is made between the Saturnioidea and the Sphingidae.

Dr. Harrison G. Dyar did not find this paper and in 1894 again discussed the subject as new and numbered the primary setae. So far as I know, this author makes the first suggestion that the position of the setae be used in classification. His observations included a few representatives of many families and his phylogeny as based on them is remarkably good. He also numbers the metathoracic setae but makes no attempt to show that the seta bearing a certain number on the abdomen is homologous with one bearing the same number on the thorax. He himself realized that the metathoracic "tubercles," i a+i b and ii a+ii b (Fig. 11), were not the homotypes of the abdominal setae i and ii (Fig. 12), and in 1901 made a definite statement to that effect. This discussion, therefore, can not be considered a contribution to the study of homotypy.

In another paper the following year the same author reported observations on the first stages of many larvae, finding that they differed considerably from following stages. By these observations he established the primary arrangement of the setae on the abdomen and demonstrated its uniformity throughout a great part of the order. A few months later, in "A Classification of Lepidoptera on Larval Characters'', he made the former work on the Frenatae apply to the setal pattern of the Jugatae. The purpose of this paper was, however, more to point out the differences between the larvae of the two suborders than to show their similarity.

O. Hofmann (1898) described the first and later instars of certain pterophorid larvae, reaching the conclusion that the thoracic and abdominal setae are homologous but that additional ones are present on the prothorax. The suggestions he makes and the reasons given are excellent. Dyar's nomenclature is used, with the result that he does not make his own conceptions as clear as if he had changed it to meet his own ideas of homology.

In response to criticism by Hofmann, Dyar (1901) finally did express an opinion on the serial homology of the setae so far as the last two thoracic and first eight abdominal segments are concerned. The table he gives, which is as follows, merely indicates his agreement with the views of Hofmann.

Numerals now applied		Should
Thorax	Abdomen	be
II and III	1 to 8	called
i a	i	i
i b	ii	ii
ii a	iii	iii
ii b	iv	iv
iii	—	v a
iv	v	v
v	vi	v b
vi	vii	vi

It will be seen that the conclusions indicated by the table agree in most particulars with those reached on later pages of this paper except in the relation of setae iv and v. Altho the point will be discussed later, it should be mentioned here that the error arises from a failure to consider the condition in Hepialus. The larvae of that genus show clearly that the missing seta near the abdominal spiracle is not between iv and v but above iv. Seta iv of the metathorax is therefore homotypic with iv of the abdomen, v with v of the abdomen, and vi of the abdomen is not represented on the thorax. Other reasons for this view will be discussed later.

Ambrose Quail (1904) discusses these particular setae, basing his opinions on the condition in the first instar of certain Hepialidae and Frenatae. He calls attention to the error mentioned above and shows Dyar's mistake concerning the true meaning of ii b. Instead of being homotypic with iv of the abdomen, it is shown to be really iii a, a seta which Dyar had either overlooked or considered of no importance.

W. T. M. Forbes' work (1910) did not cover the subject of the homotypy of the setae. The few figures he labels include errors for which he was not responsible as he had not given the subject consideration. (See discussion of theta, page 34.)

Siltala (1907) made a study of the chitinous armature, especially the setae, of caddice-worms. He finds considerable variation in the order (Trichoptera) but carefully compares the different arrangements. The setae of the first larval stage are very sparse while those of later instars are obviously special and secondary developments. In neither case can satisfactory comparisons be made with the Lepidoptera.

THE CHAETOTAXY OF A TYPICAL SEGMENT

While previous workers have drawn so-called type segments, these have never included all the setae found in larvae of this order. Their significance has been limited to particular segments or to particular groups. For example, Dyar's "typical segment" refers to the abdomen only, altho it has been extended to cover the last two thoracic segments of the larvae of Frenatae.

In order to make the following pages clear, attention should be called at this point to the diagram (Fig. 1) which shows all the primary and subprimary setae normally present on the segments of any generalized lepidopterous larva. The evidence on which this diagram is based and also the reasons for the adoption of Greek letters instead of numerals in naming the setae are given on later pages. This hypothetical type is mentioned here as a point of reference in order that it may be possible to use the setae as illustrations of the general principles on which this study of homology is based. On the same and the following plates are shown some of the modifications of the plan.

It has been necessary to introduce certain new terms in this paper and in a few cases to use the old terms in a special sense. A glossary will be found at the close of Part Two, giving the meaning of all words used in a special sense in this discussion. The explanation of plates (p. 147) gives the names and grouping of all the setae.

II. NATURE OF THE EVIDENCE

It is necessary first to outline the principles underlying attempts at any determination of homotypes. The evidence on which decisions in doubtful cases were based is discussed here, for some of the principles are not axiomatic. Their correctness will not be disputed, I am sure, by those who consider the broad basis of fact on which they rest.

DEFINITIONS

According to the Standard Dictionary, homology refers either *(a)* to "the correspondence of a part of one animal with another, determined by agreement in derivation and development from a like primitive origin," or *(b)* to homotypy, which is "the correspondence of a part or organ of one region with that of another region in the same animal." Smith, in the "Glossary of Entomology", adds the usual provision that "the organs must be identical in general structure and origin, tho they may have developed in different ways for different purposes."

There is an important difference between the homology of crustacean appendages with each other and the homology of the setae in insects. In the former case, work is based on similarity in the fundamental structure and development of the homologous organs; in the latter, only position can be considered, as the setae are all similar in structure. For that reason it is necessary to secure a little more accurate definition as a basis of work. With this in view, I suggest the following:

Two organs on different segments of the same animal are homotypic, regardless of their positions at the present time, when they have developed from homotypic organs of a generalized ancestor. In a generalized type, two similar organs on different segments are homotypes when they bear the same relations to the other organs of their respective segments.

To show that a prothoracic seta, for example, is homologous with one on the mesothorax, it is necessary to show that at one time the anlagen from which these setae were developed were in similiar positions on their respective segments. On the other hand it is equally true that, when two setae of a specialized form are in similar positions on their respective segments, a demonstration that they diverge farther and farther as we study the more and more generalized types shows that they are not true homologues but have converged in phylogenetic development. This gives to ancestry the primary importance and makes necessary a consideration of the nature of the evidence which bears on phylogeny.

DIFFICULTIES

The meagerness of the results thus far obtained on this problem is due partially to peculiar difficulties in its solution. Certain obstacles stand in the way of an accurate and complete demonstration of the homology of the setae. They are mentioned, not to emphasize the magnitude of the task, but to explain the fact that so many doubtful points remain unsettled.

The first of these difficulties is caused by the absence of intermediate stages between radically different conditions. When the tubercles* have been modified to form scoli or verrucae, it often seems impossible to determine whether differences have arisen by coalescence or by the disappearance of some of the tubercles. In many cases this is a very real problem, on whose solution depends the correctness of the conception of large groups.

Another obstacle is the lack of developmental series. In the case of wings, the tracheae which precede the veins in larval and pupal stages plainly show the relation of the adult venation to the generalized type. The single elementary instar which acts as a guide in the study of the chaetotaxy of caterpillars, however, is sometimes so unlike the mature larva in the arrangement of its setae, that it is of little assistance in interpreting their homology. The change is usually sudden and occurs at molting. Were the recapitulation more often extended over several molts the problem would be easier.

The third difficulty is one that, up to this time, has prevented progress in this field. Apparently a lepidopterous larva has three or more entirely distinct types of arrangement of the setae (Figs. 7, 8). In only a few species is there any apparent relation between the plan of the prothorax and that of the mesothorax, or between the last abdominal segment and any of the others. While this obstacle is not a serious one in classification, it has prevented thus far the determination of a satisfactory nomenclature and therefore of a working basis. Since Wilhelm Müller said in 1886 that he found ''no support for a comparison of the prothoracic setae with those of the following segments'', workers seem to have left the prothorax severely alone. They seem not to have realized that there is evidence not found in the Nymphalidae on which Müller was working.

Fortunately there are partial hints and clews to assist in surmounting each of these obstacles. Study of varied forms often yields signs of intermediate stages in position. Sometimes the single first stage, our only evidence of the past, unmistakably points the way to an interpretation we would not otherwise think of making. Again, the presence of a single unusual seta on a single segment of a generalized form will unite the setal plans of otherwise seriously differing segments. In these ways the gaps are at least partially closed and the problem is taken out of the realm of guesswork and abstraction.

---

*The word, "tubercle", is used in this paper as a general term to indicate the location of a seta, or of a definite group of setae, or a process of the body wall bearing such a group.

COMPARATIVE ANATOMY

Caterpillars may be said to bear setae in all possible positions. Their great number and uniform distribution in some species makes naming and homologizing them seem impossible. A little study of the less "hairy" ones, however, soon shows that the arrangement is quite constant and further investigation proves that they have all been derived from the same typical plan.

The method used in determining this plan was the ordinary one in problems of this kind. The setae of the prothorax, metathorax, and abdomen of the generalized members of both suborders of Lepidoptera were plotted, one segment over the other, as if all were on the same segment. It was then found that the number of setae in this composite picture (Fig. 1) was about fifteen, and that they were in approximately the same position as on the prothorax of the most generalized forms of the order.

The next problem concerns the relation of the different segments of a larva to each other and to the generalized type. It is clear from the first that the prothorax is least modified throughout the series. We can not assume, however, that the setae of the following segments of a caterpillar may be directly homologized with the type by comparing them with the prothorax of the same individual. Differentiation into the three types of arrangement must have occurred long before the suborders of Lepidoptera were differentiated from each other. The first insect with scaly wings and long maxillae probably arose from a larva possessing a different arrangement of the setae on the abdomen from that on the prothorax. It is possible that all of the thoracic segments were similar, but the abdomen was certainly distinct. In view of that fact, one easily sees that complete reliance on any single modern form is likely to lead to error. An abdominal "type" must be worked out in the way used to establish a hypothetical generalized type. Then a comparison of the thoracic and abdominal types with the general type will bring us as near as comparative anatomy can, to a correct view of the homology between the prothorax and abdomen.

ONTOGENY

That the embryological development of an animal has an important bearing on the study of its phylogeny has been recognized ever since the "recapitulation theory" was first advanced. This theory has not, however, shown the way to a complete solution of the problems of ancestry. The development of members of nearly all animal groups and that of the rarest and most peculiar forms has attracted numerous workers. Many problems still remain unsolved,—for the recapitulation is neither direct nor easy to interpret and is often covered by such a multitude of complications, reversals, and omissions that we are baffled in an attempt at their solution. For this reason, before an argument can be based on ontogeny, it must be shown that the condition discussed is necessarily a recapitulation.

When the larva of a moth hatches from the egg it is somewhat different, in most cases, from the mature caterpillar. The "woolly bear" is as naked as a cutworm and the butterfly larva could be mistaken for a tortricid. Sometimes indications of this peculiar condition remain after the first molt, but usually this glimpse of the past is as evanescent as it is surprising. Let this minute "worm" reach the second instar and nothing remains to show that the arctian was not always "hairy", or that the ancestors of the saturnian did not possess prominent scoli.

The natural supposition that this first stage is a recapitulation of the past has seldom been doubted. Several arguments, or, rather, suggestions, may however be advanced against it, and these must be disproven before this stage is admitted as evidence.

In the first place it may be urged that this stage represents an adaptive condition. While it is true that the thick setae of an arctian or the spiny processes of a nymphalid might prove an obstacle to hatching, this would merely show that the former condition had been retained in the first instar after the appearance of the new armature in later development, rather than that a new elementary stage had been acquired. At the same time such an interpretation can not give us a clue to the reason for the lack of one of the setae (mu) (cf. Figs. 29 and 31) on the abdomen of all the Frenatae in the first stage, and its presence after the first molt. Nor is it clear how the absence of theta from slightly different positions on all the segments of Hepialus (cf. Figs. 2, 3, 4 with Fig. 6) could assist in emerging from the egg. Secondary adaptation might explain a transformation in the entire style of armature but only recapitulation can suggest a reason for changes in the presence and position of a single seta.

Again, the differences between the elementary stages of different forms may be pointed out and the conclusion reached that they can not therefore represent an ancestral condition. While the first stages are not, it is true, identical throughout the order, they do not vary one-tenth as much as the mature larvae. These first instars diverge slightly in several directions from the ancestral type, while the mature larvae diverge rapidly and extensively from the type. The former are so nearly uniform that their evidence in regard to the past is invaluable.

A third position might be taken with regard to development by successive molts on the supposition that it might not constitute an ontogeny in the usual meaning of the term. At the same time it must be recognized that the instars through which a caterpillar passes are as necessary a part of its development as are the changes within the egg. Specific evidence of recapitulation in the life history of animals which molt is taken up in a later paragraph.

Constructive evidence on the recapitulation theory as applied to larval instars is considerable in amount. Some of it has been suggested in answering the objections and merely the outline of this evidence is given below. There is no need to develop the different points.

I. The instars of other Arthropoda recapitulate their ancestral history. Examples: Sacculina and its degeneration; the changes of barnacles; the zooea, mysis stages, etc., of Decapoda.

II. The phylogeny of other insects is shown by their postembryonic development. Examples: in Coccidae, the presence of the anal ring in the nymphs of Kermesinae, and the appearance of primary and secondary pygidia in certain Diaspinae; in Coleoptera, the campodeiform larva preceding the eruciform in certain cases.

III. The development of the setal plan of lepidopterous larvae itself bears prima facie evidence that it constitutes a recapitulation. 1. All the Frenatae are almost identical in the first instar when that stage is different from later ones. 2. The first stage of the Jugatae is much nearer that of the Frenatae than later stages are. 3. Larvae with tufted setae, as arctians, usually possess only the primary setae before the first molt and these are in the typical position. 4. The armature of the larvae of Nymphalidae and certain other butterflies or specialized Lepidoptera is not homologous with that of the moths but is preceded in the first stage by the setae in the typical position. 5. The absence of theta on all the segments of Hepialus and the Frenatae in the first stage, and its presence on all the segments of Hepialus and on the thorax of Frenatae in the next stage, can have no other meaning than that this seta is a later arrival than those which are present from the time of hatching and that it has become established in the Frenatae on the thorax only. 6. Setae are distinct in the first instar of Sphingidae, Dioptidae, and other groups, but are very much reduced or wanting later. At the same time their descent from forms in which the setae are distinct is unquestionable.

The writer has become convinced from many facts of which the preceding are only examples, that the first-stage larva of Lepidoptera represents the ancestral type; that the arrangement of the setae in this instar is essentially the same their ancestors bore in some remote antiquity. While it does not extend back to that distant age when all the segments bore the same setal plan, it furnishes a connecting link between that period and the present day. I have no hesitancy in denominating, as Dyar does, a seta as only "subprimary" when it is constantly wanting in the first stage, however invariable may be its presence in the second. For the same reason I can not consider a subprimary seta of a specialized group as homologous with a primary one of a generalized group. Such an homology is entirely inconsistent with the recapitulation theory.

In a word, the arrangement of the setae in the larvae of the Lepidoptera gives us every reason to believe and no cause to deny the hypothesis Weismann expressed in 1876: "New characters first appear in the last stage of individual development; these move back gradually into the earlier stages and so crowd out the older characters until the latter finally disappear."

VARIATION

In many cases the presence of secondary or tufted setae is confusing in determining the location of the primary ones. The acquisition of additional scattered setae in one species or genus is a very common occurrence and caution should be used in giving this character as bounding any group. The condition in Drepanidae, Thyatiridae, and Geometridae furnishes good examples.

When several primary setae are united by being surrounded by a chitinized plate they have a tendency to vary in number. This is true of the Pi group on the proleg-bearing segments of the abdomen. Pi itself consisted originally of two primary setae but tau is usually associated with them. In many Noctuidae the three are borne on a chitinized leg plate. In notodontians, arctians, and other groups specialized from the ancestral noctuid type, this plate bears many setae, none of which can be homologized with the primary ones (cf. Figs. 31 and 33).

III. APPLICATION OF THE EVIDENCE

As stated above, two setae on different segments of the same or different larvae are homologous, regardless of their position at the present time, when they have descended from the same or homologous organs of a generalized ancestor. It follows from the definition that no single case of homology can be absolutely proven. No combination of circumstances is sufficient to show, beyond the shadow of a doubt, that two setae on a modern larva are descendants from the same or homologous structures of some extinct ancestor. Nature's directions are, however, sufficiently clear to remove the problems completely from the

realm of speculation. Let us consider for a moment the nature and kind
of these indications and their use as evidence on a correct nomenclature
of the setae.

APPLICATION OF PRINCIPLES

Similar position in all modern forms.—When a group of setae are
in similar positions throughout the entire series of mature caterpillars,
we may conclude that they are homologous with each other. If further
evidence does not point distinctly in some other direction, we can not go
back of this stand. Practically every segment of every caterpillar bears
one seta near the medioventral line on each side. This the writer calls
sigma and it is clear that in these setae we are dealing with truly homologous organs; that on the thoracic and abdominal segments in Hepialus
as well as the Frenatae, these ventral setae are homotypes.

Similar position on certain segments of all modern forms. A nearly
uniform arrangement of the setae on the prothorax of practically all the
members of the order is excellent evidence that this arrangement is
ancestral and that it has not arisen through convergent development.
On the other hand, such a condition cannot bear on the relations of the
segments to one another.

*Similar arrangement on all the segments in the most generalized
groups.* Every structure of Hepialus points to the view that this genus
is one of the most generalized of Lepidoptera. While distinctly in a different suborder, it bears much evidence that it is closer to the ancestral
type than are most of the Frenatae. When we find in it, therefore, that
the relations (Figs. 5, 6, 13, 14) of alpha, beta, and rho, to each other and
to the boundaries of the segments, are identical throughout the body,
we have reason to believe that they are homologous in spite of their
changed position in the Frenatae on the mesothorax and metathorax. It
simply remains to derive the condition found on these two segments
of Frenatae from that shown by the same two segments of Hepialus,
and again we have a complete series of homologues.

Similar position on all the segments of newly hatched larvae.
The bearing of the setal arrangement of first-stage larvae was discussed
under the subject "Ontogeny". Homologizing a seta never present in
this stage with another that is present cannot usually be admitted as
justifiable. On the abdomen of Hepialus (Figs. 6, 13) there are three
setae, theta, kappa, and eta, in a long diagonal row caudad and ventrad of
the spiracle. Of these, the upper one is absent from the first stage on all
the segments and therefore, according to Weismann's hypothesis, may
be assumed to be of more recent origin. It would certainly be incorrect
to homologize it with any primary seta of generalized Frenatae.

Series of changes. Ordinarily two setae in the same relative position on their respective segments are considered homologous. Two setae in different positions may be homologous, however, if they have reached these new positions by migrations during phylogeny. In many cases an intermediate location is shown by the first instar, while in others a large number of mature larvae will show a complete series of steps in the migration from the old position to the new one.

CHOICE OF A NOMENCLATURE

At the present time Roman numerals are in more or less general use as a means of denominating the setae of lepidopterous larvae. They were introduced by Dyar and have been retained, largely in their original sense, partly because the great majority of recent papers describing caterpillars have been written by this worker. The wide distribution of his papers and the undoubted accuracy of his observation would lead the present writer to adopt his nomenclature if that were possible. For several reasons, however, it seems that the use of numbers in this connection is no longer desirable.

In the first place the abdomen of Frenatae, upon which the numeral system was based, can not represent the original type. In some particulars it differs radically from the same segments of the Jugatae. Attempts to derive the setal plan of the thoracic segments from .this arrangement and to find any evidence for such a derivation have been fruitless. The original type segment, or better, the potential arrangement from which the modern plan has been derived, must have included a greater instead of a smaller number of setae than are at present found on the meso- and metathorax. Many of the thoracic setae are undoubtedly as primary and as ancestral as those on the abdomen, and the same is true of some of the additional setae shown on Hepialus; therefore, if Dyar's numerals are used we should be compelled either to give letters and subnumerals to primary setae simply because they are not present on the abdomen of modern caterpillars, or to adopt his scheme for the abdomen of Frenatae and apply a different one to all other body-segments and to the Jugatae. Neither of these methods would fulfill our hope of a uniform nomenclature based on homology and applicable to all the segments of all lepidopterous larvae.

In the second place any series of names which have as definite an order as numbers is sure to be misleading and is likely to prejudice one's views in regard to homology. The mere use of numerals beginning at the mediodorsal line tends to cause one to give the upper of two setae the smaller numeral and to neglect the fact that some setae are absent. In wing venation, it is found that when numbers are used, workers tend to neglect studying out the true homology. This danger is still more apparent in work on the setae, for whereas it is rare to find a branch of radius, for example, crossing media and reaching the margin of the wing back of the latter, it is an ordinary occurrence for seta ii to be found above i, for seta v to take almost any position with respect to iv, and for vii to consist of one, two, three, or many setae, either approximate to each other, or decidedly remote in position.

In place of the numerals now in use the writer suggests Greek letters. They combine a quickly written character for labeling plates and an easily pronounced word with which all scientific men are familiar. A special letter can be introduced for a subprimary seta in a limited group without disarranging the system. The alphabetical order is not so fixed in the mind as to prejudice one in regard to homology. At the same time the confusion introduced by the papers of Quail and Forbes in Dyar's system is avoided and, as long as the Greek letters are retained in the original sense, the meaning will be absolutely clear.

As it is convenient to have a single term for groups of setae and for compound tubercles, such as scoli, the writer capitalizes the letter indicating one of the more constant of the primary setae composing the group. For example a verruca bearing a tuft of setae developed from the group consisting of theta, kappa, and eta, is known as the verruca of the Kappa group and labeled "K" (cf. Figs. 7 and 25). In cases where there is doubt about the number of primary setae from which a scolus or verruca is developed, the capital letter is usually employed. This method is particularly valuable where it is impossible or disadvantageous to indicate the components of the group. The names of the groups and the setae composing them are given on page 39.

As mentioned on a previous page, a seta is known as primary when it is present on the newly hatched larva. If it first appears after one of the molts but is fairly constant, it is known as subprimary, e.g., mu, theta, etc.   Secondary setae are those which have no constant position, are more or less numerous and scattered, are not ancestral, and bear absolutely no relation to the primary setae. They are very rarely found in the first instar. The individual setae of a tuft borne on a verruca are not given distinctive names, the group itself being called primary or subprimary according to its origin. The numerous setae which it bears are not considered secondaries.

IV. SETAL ARRANGEMENT IN THE PRINCIPAL SUPERFAMILIES

In this section the larval chaetotaxy of a number of typical species is described. Each seta is named when it is first mentioned in the description, the same name being applied to its homotypes on other segments and other larvae as they are reached. While it is not feasible to discuss their homology in detail in this place, some of the evidence supporting the view expressed is usually given, except where the correspondence is entirely obvious. Section V then takes up each seta in turn, follows it through its principal migrations and modifications, and briefly summarizes the evidence for each case of homotypy.

SUBORDER JUGATAE

Of the suborder Jugatae the writer has studied in detail but one genus, Hepialus, and the description will be limited to it. The setae of larval Micropterygidae have been so reduced by leaf-mining habits that conclusions can not be based on them. Hepialus, on the other hand, seems still to be generalized and, as its wings gave Comstock the clew to the ancestral venation, so its chaetotaxy has suggested the generalized setal plan.

Had Dyar studied the prothorax of the larvae of this genus as carefully as he did the other segments the following description would not be necessary. As it is, the writer is compelled to rely on his figure of the first stage; for up to the present time no newly hatched larvae have been available for study. As this first stage is essential in the determination of homology, my results are based on the assumption that his figures are correct. Descriptions of the later stages in this paper were made from *Hepialus humuli,* verified by comparison with *H. hectus* and *H. lupulinus,* two or more individuals of each species being studied.

First Instar

[Figs. 2, 3, 4]

The prothorax of the newly hatched larva (Fig. 2) bears six setae above the spiracle, two in front of it, two between it and the leg, and one in front of the leg. No ventral setae are indicated. Those above the spiracle are in two transverse rows of three setae each, those in the caudal row being much closer together and farther ventrad than those of the cephalic row. As shown on the figures, I have named those on the cephalic row, alpha, gamma, and epsilon, and the caudal group, beta, delta, and rho, beginning in each case near the dorsomeson. In front of the spiracle, kappa and eta represent the Kappa group, and between the spiracle and the leg the two setae, pi and nu, form the Pi group. The seta in front of the leg is tau.

The mesothorax and metathorax (Fig. 3) are practically identical in their arrangement. As there is no spiracle, let us describe the setae as above and below kappa, the single seta at the level of the prothoracic spiracle. Above it are only five setae, two in a cephalic and three in a caudal row. The homology is perfectly evident, gamma, the middle of the three setae of the prothorax, being the only absentee, and alpha, beta, delta, rho, and epsilon having the same position as before. Below kappa is located pi, the caudal seta of the Pi group. Tau occupies the same position as before.

We thus find that all the thoracic segments in this instar are arranged on the same plan but that the prothorax bears three more setae, gamma, eta, and nu, than the other two segments. Whether these setae have been lost from the second and third segments or added to the first will be discussed in a succeeding paragraph.

On the abdomen (Fig. 4) above the spiracle there are only four setae, two in each transverse row. The cephalic row, exactly as in the metathorax, consists of alpha and epsilon, but in the caudal row delta is wanting. Four of the six dorsal prothoracic setae are then retained on the abdomen. Of the lateral setae, kappa and eta are both present as on the prothorax but they are widely separated. It will be shown later that this separation is not of great importance in showing the ancestral condition or the homotypy, for on the abdomen of the Microlepidoptera, kappa and eta are approximate as they are on the prothorax. Unquestionably they have been derived from the same source on all the body segments.

At the base of the proleg are found two cephalolateral setae and one cephalic seta. The first two are almost directly behind pi on the metathorax and clearly represent pi and nu. As the other is in front of the proleg and bears the same relation to it that tau does to the thoracic leg, it doubtless represents that seta. We may therefore conclude that the arrangement of the abdominal setae is homotypic with that of the prothoracic.

Later Instars

[Figs. 5, 6, 13, 14]

The mature larva of Hepialus differs in some important particulars from the condition in the first stage. Most of these differences were pointed out by Dyar and their bearing on phylogeny was discussed. Our point of view is somewhat different from his, for we are considering homotypy, a field which he did not enter.

The most striking change brought about at the first molt is the appearance of a certain seta, theta, on each segment. This is always caudad of kappa and dorsad of it on all but the prothoracic segment. It is the best established subprimary seta in the whole order, for it suddenly appears at the first molt on all the segments of Hepialus and on the mesothorax and metathorax of Frenatae. Another late arrival is omega, situated between nu and tau on the abdomen. Whether it is present in the first stage on the thorax, I do not know, but in the mature larva it is on the ventral surface of the thoracic as well as of the abdominal segments.

The mature larva of *Hepialus humuli* may then be described as follows:

Prothorax (Fig. 5). Six setae are located above the spiracle and three in front of it. All of these are placed on the cervical shield, which extends ventrad to the level of the middle of the spiracle. Along the cephalic border of the shield are five setae the upper three of which are alpha, gamma, and epsilon, as described on the first-stage larva. The lower two, kappa and eta, in front of the dorsal margin of the spiracle, are lateral in position and belong to the Kappa group. On the caudal margin of the shield is a group of three setae, beta, delta, and rho, arranged in a curved line directly above the spiracle. Slightly separated from these is another, ventrad of the lower end of this line. The latter is theta, the third member of the Kappa group, and is always associated with kappa and eta.

Near the coxa of the leg is a chitinized plate bearing two setae, pi and nu, representing the constant and important Pi group. In front of the leg are certain small setae, usually two in number, with a third sometimes added. These I call the Tau group, for they are extremely variable and it is difficult to homologize the individual setae. They are, however, not related to each other in the same sense as the members of the Kappa group, Pi group, etc. The one closest to Pi may be called omega, and the others, tau and phi. Behind the coxa, as in all caterpillars, sigma is present near the ventromeson.

Mesothorax and Metathorax (Fig. 5). These segments are each divided into three annulets, marked distinctly on the dorsal half of the segment but partially lost on the ventral. On the first of these is found a group of three minute setae, which must represent gamma or a structure developed in its place. As it is in the position of gamma it is most convenient to give it that name altho the evidence is not conclusive. The middle annulet bears two setae, one near the dorsomeson, the other directly caudad of the prothoracic spiracle. These, as in the first stage, are clearly homologous with alpha and epsilon. Assuming that the homology suggested in regard to the first annulet is correct, we now have the entire row, alpha, gamma and epsilon, accounted for.

The third annulet bears three subdorsal setae and two lateral ones. The three subdorsal are plainly beta, delta, and rho, as on the prothorax. They are somewhat more dorsal in position and not so close together, but otherwise clearly represent the same structures. The two lateral setae are in the same position as the Kappa group. The caudal one is clearly theta, for it was not found on the newly hatched larva; but the other may be either kappa or eta. I have labeled it kappa, altho there is no evidence in this one species that it may not have developed from eta instead. We shall see, however, that eta, when present on the thorax, as in most of the Frenatae, takes a position quite distinct from that shown here, while kappa is usually found in this place. The homology as given, is therefore undoubtedly correct.

Laterad of the leg and close to the coxa is a single seta, often borne on a chitinized plate. This is pi, the only representative of the Pi group ever found on the mesothorax except in a few cases. The Tau group and sigma are also present.

Abdomen. The relation of the type of arrangement of the setae of the abdomen (Fig. 13) to that of the thorax can not be determined from a study of the mature larva alone. This is due to the addition of several new setae at the first molt and the changed position of others. As in the first instar, there are four setae above the level of the spiracle, but these do not so clearly represent the two transverse rows as before. The ventral seta of the caudal row, rho, had migrated cephalad to the middle of the segment even before the first molt and is now found very close to epsilon and associated with it above the spiracle. The fact that this is actually rho and that it has come from the caudal part of the segment can not be doubted after seeing figures of the newly hatched larva and studying the record of this seta throughout other members of the order.

In the spiracular region are three setae in a diagonal line, theta and kappa caudad of the spiracle and eta some distance ventrad. Kappa and eta were noted in the first instar but theta was missing. The latter's relative position on the abdomen is the same as that of its homotype on the thorax.

Below eta the maximum number of setae on any segment except the last is five. These are arranged differently as we pass caudad. In *Hepialus humuli* all are present on the first six abdominal segments, but one of those on the first segment is much smaller than the others. It is entirely missing from this segment of *H. lupulinus* and *H. hectus*. On the second segment the arrangement is more typical. Two setae, pi and nu, are close together near the middle of the segment and only slightly more ventrad than their homotypes on the thorax. Sigma is present as usual near the ventromeson. This leaves only two setae, and they are in the same position here as the Tau group on the thorax, so the entire homology is clear, as labeled on the plate.

On the proleg-bearing segments, omega varies between a mesocephalic position at the base of the leg in some species to a laterocephalic location in others. In the latter position it is quite closely associated with the Pi group and seems to belong to it rather than to the group from which it was derived. On segments 7, 8, and 9, it is, however, wanting, so that these segments bear four subventral setae, nu and pi representing the still bisetose Pi group, tau alone remaining of the group which bears its name, and, as usual, sigma near the medioventral line.

In many caterpillars the ninth abdominal segment shows a very puzzling condition, analogous to that on the mesothorax. There is a tendency for the setae to arrange themselves in a single transverse line, challenging the investigator to say which is which. The larvae of Hepialus (Fig. 14), however, have not undergone so much change, and homologizing the setae on this body-segment is not so difficult. As usual alpha and beta are found near the mediodorsal line with rho and theta below them. Epsilon, altho present on the preceding segments, is wanting here, but it is such an evanescent seta that its absence in this place is not surprising. Kappa and eta are somewhat closer together and farther caudad and dorsad than before, but the homology is clear. This leaves only the subventral setae, which, as was stated in the last paragraph, are identical with those on segments 7 and 8.

The most difficult problem of all still remains and we can give it only a partial answer. Had we all the ancestors of Hepialus there might still be a doubt as to the meaning of the anal segment. Is there a tenth segment and then a telson representing the eleventh? Does the proleg belong to the tenth or to the eleventh segment and does it bear the setae of both segments or of only one of them? What is the origin of the setae on the caudal aspect? The condition in Hepialus larvae is as follows:

On the dorsal half of the last abdominal segment (Fig. 14) is a semicircular plate whose diameter is the cephalic border of the segment. On each side of the meson this plate bears three setae, two in a longitudinal line comparable to the position of alpha and beta on the other segments, and one farther laterad and cephalad. Between the plate and the anus is a pair of fleshy projections, the suranal lobes, each bearing one seta on its caudal aspect. Below the anus another pair of lobes and the prolegs bear a total of eight setae. Two of these are on the caudal aspect of the ventral lobe, four on the lateral aspect and one on the caudal aspect of the proleg, and the other cephalad of the proleg.

In the first place it should be noted that while it is possible to name these structures, there is no great amount of evidence as to their true homology. If we call those on the plate epsilon, beta, and rho, then the one on the suranal lobes must be theta. This would indicate that the tenth segment is very similar to the ninth and gives us a hint as to the other setae. The one on the mesocephalic aspect of the proleg would thus be tau, and the one in a mesocaudal position, sigma, while the four on the lateral aspect would represent pi, nu, omega, and phi. Calling the two setae behind the proleg kappa and eta, completes the series.

These setae have been named not so much to express an opinion regarding their homology as to show that only one set is present. There is only one more seta (phi) on this segment than on any of the other proleg-bearing ones and one (epsilon) is missing. We may consequently conclude that the setae give no evidence for considering the anal segment to be composed of more than one metamere either in its dorsal or ventral portions. The proof is especially clear either that the suranal plate does not represent a telson, or that if it does the dorsal half of segment 10 has been entirely suppressed. Those who have asserted that the setae show that this segment consists of more than one somite have not studied carefully the data on which their opinions were based.

Conclusions from a Study of Jugatae

Hepialus has been considered in detail because it is very close to the typical form and represents an entire suborder, the Jugatae. There are some primitive features about it which give us a clue to the homology in other groups. This is especially true of the thoracic segments, whose relation to the abdomen and to each other would be wholly in the dark without this form. The prothorax shows the same essential type of arrangement as the other segments. It has been a failure to study Hepialus carefully that has caused Müller, Dyar, Quail, and Forbes to omit the prothorax in their work on the setae and to consider its chaetotaxy as of wholly different origin.

SUBORDER FRENATAE

The chaetotaxy of the larvae of this suborder has been described in detail by Dyar, and he has also compared it with the setal plan of the Jugatae. A brief consideration of those modifications of the plan which might be confusing in a determination of homotypes is all that is necessary here.

Bombycoidea

The Noctuidae are considered first, not because they are the most generalized but because the writer has studied no other larvae in the first instar.* The setal plan of *Feltia gladiaria* in this stage shows a close correspondence to that of the newly hatched Hepialus larva. On the prothorax (Fig. 17) eta of the Kappa group, all the Tau group, and sigma are wanting. Otherwise the homology is clear. The mesothorax and metathorax (Fig. 18) show a condition which has probably been developed on account of the great mobility of these segments. The setae are in a single transverse row. Above kappa, located caudad of the prothoracic spiracle, are four setae instead of the five borne by Hepialus. The missing one proves to be delta, for the close correspondence with the abdomen shows that the dorsal two are alpha and beta; and the others are undoubtedy epsilon and rho, which are usually associated together on all segments. Below kappa is pi, near the proleg. As on the prothorax, the Tau group and sigma are wanting.

The abdomen (Figs. 19, 20, 29) shows alpha and beta in their usual positions near the dorsomeson except on the first few segments, where they are more nearly in a transverse row, similar to their arrangement on the metathorax. Just dorsad of the spiracle is rho, a well-developed seta, and in most cases a minute point representing epsilon. The latter, known as iii a in the literature, is often considered subprimary, but the presence of this rudiment, which Bacot (Quail, 1904) says is of common, if not universal, occurrence in all stages of the larvae of Frenatae, proves it to be primary. Its small size is the result of reduction, rho having migrated caudad to the region it once occupied. The other abdominal setae are just as in the first-stage Hepialus. In Feltia, tau is not present, but in most Frenatae it is said to be associated with nu and pi in all instars and is usually considered a member of the Pi group. Its absence from the first, seventh, and eighth abdominal segments is a common occurrence. Sigma is located near the medioventral line as usual.

The homology of the setae of segment 9 (Fig. 30) may be solved by a comparison with the same segment of the mature Hepialus larva and a study of other species which form connecting links between the two conditions. The evidence for considering the most cephalic of the subdorsal setae as alpha, will be given in the next section. Beta is much closer to the dorsomeson, as on the prothorax. The presence in some species of a minute seta (epsilon) close to the third seta shows the latter

---

*Careful descriptions of first-stage larvae of many other groups have been published, the prothorax usually being omitted. Since sending this paper to the printer, the first instar of *Prionoxystus robiniae* (Cossidae) has been examined by the writer. Its prothorax is identical with that shown in figures of Hepialus in this stage, differing from noctuid larvae in the presence of two setae, instead of only one, in the Kappa group.

to be rho. This leaves only three setae, which are certainly kappa, pi, and sigma. All of these conclusions are based on series of intermediate stages.

Segment 10 bears only one seta less than in Hepialus but the homology is not clear.

The mature Feltia (Figs. 21 to 24, 31, 32) shows certain modifications of the chaetotaxy of the first stage. The arrival of theta and gamma on the mesothorax and metathorax, the first caudodorsad of kappa, the other near the cephalic border of the segment, are the only changes duplicated on Hepialus. On all the thoracic segments eta appears ventrad of kappa. As it was not present at all on the last two segments of Jugatae, the condition here shows that since its establishment on the abdomen it has arisen on the thorax, where, under Weismann's law, it has not yet reached the first instar. Finally mu, the most recent arrival of all the subprimaries, appears caudoventrad of eta on the first eight abdominal segments.

A significant change in position also occurs after the first molt. Epsilon, located below alpha and gamma in the cephalic subdorsal row of the prothorax in the first stage, now appears close to rho above the spiracle. This migration distinguishes the Bombycoidea from the Microlepidoptera, for in the latter group epsilon remains near the cephalic border of the prothoracic shield.

Microlepidoptera

Altho the differences between the Noctuidae and the Microlepidoptera are not great, the latter are more generalized in some important particulars. These are best shown by Pseudanaphora (Figs. 7, 8, 15, 16), a member of one of the most generalized families of the order. On the prothorax theta is present, so that all three setae of the Kappa group are accounted for, just as in Hepialus. On the abdomen, kappa and eta are at the same level but still distant, altho in all the higher micros these setae are close together below the spiracle. As in the noctuid abdomen, mu is present and theta is wanting. Segment 9 shows nearly as many setae as in Hepialus, there being only two important differences; the absence of tau and theta, and the presence of mu caudoventrad of eta as on the other segments.

Other Groups

The high specialization of the armature of saturnian, sphingid, and butterfly larvae lessens their value as evidence on the homology of the setae. The first instar is usually similar to that of the Noctuidae. Only one serious problem is presented, viz., the origin of the scolus Kappa in the Saturnioidea. Whether this consists of kappa and eta or eta alone is a disputed point, altho the first instar seems to indicate the correctness of the former view.

V. Primary and Subprimary Setae

In the following discussion of the setae, the evidence for each case of homotypy is briefly summarized. The plan followed is that already outlined herein under the title, "Application of the Evidence." Other authors have indicated various conceptions of homotypy in labeling their figures but none have presented proof, except in one case, the brief paper by Quail mentioned in the introduction. As the evidence on all the important points is conclusive, the retention of an unnatural or uncertain nomenclature is no longer defensible.

Alpha. The position of this seta as given in the descriptions of the groups is so clear that a few words here will suffice. Originally alpha seems to have been farther dorsad as well as farther cephalad than any other seta. This is now true on all the segments of Hepialus, on the abdomen of nearly all Frenatae, and on the prothorax of many Tineidae and Yponomeutidae. The prothorax shows beta nearer the meson than alpha in nearly all the higher Frenatae, but this is clearly a later migration.

Alpha is always present in the first stage and is therefore primary. It is one of the most persistent setae and usually forms a verruca or scolus in species bearing these structures. Whether it is present or absent on the last two thoracic segments of Frenatae will be discussed under "Beta" on a later page.

On the ninth abdominal segment of most Frenatae, alpha is located farther laterad than beta, and in the Macrolepidoptera, this condition has gone back into the first instar. But in Hepialus (Fig. 14), Scardia (Fig. 54), Thyris (Fig. 55), and other genera, it is still as close to the dorsomeson as on the other abdominal segments. In Pseudanaphora (Fig. 16) the lateral migration has already begun and in certain Pyralididae (Fig. 49) it is carried to its greatest extent. In many families the location of this seta is a character of importance in the classification of genera (cf. Pyralididae, Tortricidae, etc., Part Two). The close association with rho in some cases seems to cast doubt on the view that this seta is homologous with alpha; but the position in generalized larvae, the complete set of intermediate stages connecting it with its other locations, the variation between the original and later positions within limited groups, and the fact that beta, epsilon, and rho are otherwise accounted for, show unquestionably that this seta must be alpha.

Beta. On the prothorax as well as the abdomen beta is always the dorsal seta of the caudal row. Its position varies from that in Hepialus

(Fig. 5), where it is about half way between the spiracle and the dorso-meson, to that in most Frenatae (Fig. 21), where it is closer to the dorsomeson than any other seta of the segment. Intermediate stages are shown by Yponomeutidae (Fig. 35) and Acrolophidae (Fig. 7).

The specialization of the mesothorax and metathorax of Frenatae has been mentioned. No intermediate stages exist to show the relations between the setal plan of these segments of Hepialus and those of Frena-tae. A comparison of the thoracic with the abdominal segments of the newly hatched larva of Feltia (Figs. 18, 19, 20, 29, 30), however, indi-cates the direction the migration has taken. Segments 6, 7, and 8 show alpha and beta in their normal positions while on segments 1 and 2 beta is almost directly ventrad of alpha. The large number of groups in which these two setae are associated in the abdomen, either by being borne on a single pinaculum, or uniting to form a single verruca, shows that they may easily become adjacent. The conclusion is therefore justified that the two dorsal setae of the mesothorax and metathorax are alpha and beta, in spite of their changed position. Hofmann, Dyar and Quail agree that this is the true condition.

Gamma. This seems to be a comparatively new seta on all but the prothorax, where it has become established. The newly hatched larva bears it only on the one segment and there its position is constant. It is often represented on meso- and metathoracic and abdominal segments as a more or less minute subprimary seta near the cephalic border of the segment and in Hepialus is associated with two other smaller ones. While there is some doubt about the accuracy of considering a primary seta of the prothorax homotypic with the subprimary one of other seg-ments, the fact that the two bear exactly the same relations to the other structures of the segment makes it inadvisable to use a different name. This will be discussed under "Eta" on a later page. The probability is that gamma is a more recent seta than the other primaries and be-came first established on the prothorax, the order of appearance on the different segments now being shown by ontogeny.

Delta. Between beta and rho on the prothorax of all caterpillars and also on the other thoracic segments of Hepialus is delta, a seta never found in any other position or on any other segment. If ancestral, it has since become lost on the abdomen of all lepidopterous larvae and on the last two thoracic segments of all Frenatae.

Epsilon. The prothoracic segments of Hepialus and Pseudana-phora bear the third seta of the cephalic row in its typical position. In connection with rho it goes through various changes which are some-times hard to follow on the other body-segments but are evident on the prothorax. In the Tortricidae (Fig. 39), Aegeriidae, and Yponomeutidae (Fig. 35), this seta remains constant in position while rho moves forward toward it. This is distinctly noticeable in Plutella while in *Atteva aurea* (Fig. 36) it has scarcely been begun. The opposite movement is to be noted in all Macrolepidoptera. The newly hatched larva of Feltia shows rho and epsilon in their normal positions distant from each other. In the mature larva, however, epsilon has migrated back to rho, leaving only alpha and gamma remaining in the cephalic subdorsal group.

On the mesothorax and metathorax of Frenatae, epsilon and rho are again found associated. Like alpha and beta they have yielded to the mobility of this part of the body and been crowded to the middle of the segments. The first stage of Hepialus and Feltia show that epsilon is the upper of the two and rho the lower. Both prothoracic and abdominal segments of Hepialus and *Cossus cossus* prove that epsilon was originally above the level of rho and that its present position ventrad of that seta on the abdomen of many of the species we know today has come about through migration.

On the abdomen of Hepialus, the presence and large size of epsilon in the first as well as later instars creates a serious problem if that seta be considered missing from its usual position in the first stage of Frenatae. I have been unable to detect it in the newly hatched Feltia larva but according to Quail (1904), who quotes A. Bacot, it is of general occurrence in all instars of Frenatae. The probability is, therefore, that it is disappearing from the abdomen and is retained in its former vigor only by Hepialus and *Cossus cossus*. There seems to be no evidence that it is in any sense subprimary.

Rho. The principal migrations of rho have been described in the discussion of epsilon. It is present in all instars on all segments of all caterpillars except when obscured in later stages by a secondary armature. Usually it is associated with epsilon when that seta is present. In species bearing verrucae, epsilon never forms one distinct from that of rho, except sometimes on the mesothorax and metathorax.

Theta. The dorsocaudal seta of the Kappa group needs consideration merely to prevent its confusion with other setae. No question can be raised as to its homotypy on the segments of Hepialus, where it is subprimary throughout, in all cases being dorsad and caudad of the primary kappa. The same is true on all thoracic segments of the tineoid series of Microlepidoptera and on the meso- and metathorax of Pyralididæ and Macrolepidoptera, where it is present and subprimary.

Some confusion might arise concerning it on the abdomen of Frenatae in those cases where kappa is well toward the upper border of the spiracle. The fact that kappa is usually much lower down, and is often associated with eta, indicates the error of a view which would call this seta theta. This is further emphasized by the subprimary nature of theta and by the fact that eta and kappa already have homologues on Hepialus without the use of theta. Forbes' (1910) error on this point was rather far reaching so far as homotypy is concerned. He gives only four figures, but in the setae epsilon, theta, kappa, eta, and mu, there are four cases* in which the same label is given in one place to a primary and in another to a subprimary seta. Most of these associations would be very difficult to explain and they are wholly unnecessary. The mistakes are due, not to errors in observation, but to a failure to take the primitive first stage into account.

Kappa. This is a fundamental, ancestral, primary seta and is readily transformed into a scolus or verruca. It occupies a position about the level of the spiracle and is almost never absent. In forming verrucae it is often associated with theta and eta, and on the prothorax of most of the Microlepidoptera a chitinized pinaculum bears all three. In specialized Microlepidoptera kappa and eta are always adjacent on the abdomen, where they take all possible positions with respect to each other. In most cases the dorsal of the two is called kappa.

On segment 9 kappa is obsolete in certain Pyralididae. The beginning of the reduction is shown in Phycitinae (Fig. 46) where eta is located on the same pinaculum with kappa and mu but is much larger than the other two. In Pyraustinae (Fig. 49) only eta remains. This condition is not sufficient, however, to justify us in calling the sole representative of the Kappa group on the ninth abdominal segment of Noctuidae, "eta", for here the position on the newly hatched larva, especially in its relation to rho and pi, shows that it is the caudal rather than the cephalic seta of the group which has been retained. (See Fig. 30.)

Eta. On the meso- and metathoracic segments of the Frenatae, eta, like theta, appears at the first molt. It is below kappa and is often associated with it. On Hepialus it is wanting on the mesothorax and metathorax but present on the prothorax. At the time of the separation of the Jugatae from the Frenatae it had appeared only on the prothorax and abdomen or had been lost on the other thoracic segments. In the latter place it has since become established in the Frenatae after the first instar.

This is one of two cases where it has seemed necessary to consider

---

*These are: iii (primary in all except Fig. 4) ; iv (primary on Figs. 4, 5, and 34, subprimary on Fig. 33) ; v (primary on Figs. 5, 33, and 34, subprimary on Fig. 4) ; vi (primary on Fig. 33, subprimary on Figs. 5 and 34).

a subprimary seta on one segment the homotype of a primary one on another. The fact that in Hepialus eta is present on both the prothorax and abdomen but that there is no seta with which it can possibly be homologous on the mesothorax and metathorax, shows that in the latter place its homotype has either been lost or has never appeared. The same conclusion is indisputable after a study of first-stage Frenatae. Since the separation of the two suborders a new seta has appeared on the caudal thoracic segments in line with eta of other parts of the body. This new seta bears the same relation to the other structures of the segment as eta does and associates with kappa in the same characteristic way. While its later appearance makes it doubtful whether the meso- thoracic seta should be called a homotype of the one on the abdomen, it is clear that no object would be served by merely attaching to it a new name. We therefore depart to that extent from a strict interpre- tation of our definition of homotypy.

Pi. Considerable confusion might exist at first in regard to the homology of this and neighboring setae. The description of the ventral half of the larva of Hepialus shows that the homology there is evident enough. Any other interpretation would involve one in endless compli- cations and would necessitate a total neglect of the generalized first larval stage.

In Frenatae, however, the prolegs are much farther mesad than the thoracic legs and the setae of the two regions have a less apparent relation to each other. This is complicated by the arrival of mu which is directly caudad of the thoracic pi and appears to be analogous with it. Fortunately the condition in the newly hatched larva proves the analogy to be more apparent than real, for mu is not present in the first instar. This is so constant a character that Dyar distinguishes the Jugatae from the Frenatae by the presence of this seta, ''vi'', after the first molt in the latter group while it never appears in the former. In spite of this fact, Dyar, Forbes, and others usually label pi on the thorax, ''vi'', indicating that it may be homotypic with mu of the abdo- men. For that reason the group requires more extended discussion than the others have received. In the following summary of the evi- dence on this point, ''Pi'' is used for the Pi group of one or two setae at the base of the thoracic legs, ''mu'' for the subprimary on the abdo- men, and ''vii'' (following Dyar) for the lateral two of the group of three setae on the prolegs which we are convinced are homotypic with ''Pi''.

Pi must be homotypic with vii in Hepialus for mu is not present. (Figs. 5 and 6.)

The first instar of larval Frenatae indicates the homotypy of Pi and vii, for no other interpretation is possible in the absence of mu (Figs. 17, 18, 19, 29.)

Pi and vii, in addition to the fact that both are primary, are both "double" in all stages on the prothoracic and abdominal segments and sometimes on the mesothorax and metathorax, while mu is always single.

The multiple nature of Pi and vii is indicated by the newly hatched larva of Panorpa, of the Mecoptera, described by E. P. Felt, 1895. Its prothorax bears the same setal plan as that of lepidopterous larvae and while the setae of the other segments of Panorpa are reduced in number the fundamental arrangement is the same. On every segment there is a pinaculum bearing four to six setae in a longitudinal row situated at the base of the leg or the proleg as the case may be. The fact that this is the first stage, all the setae being lost later, and that the Mecoptera are usually considered more generalized than the Lepidoptera, would seem to indicate that Pi originated as a multisetiferous tubercle and that the setae had been reduced to the definite number two on modern caterpillars.

Scolus-bearing larvae also indicate the homotypy of Pi on the thorax to the group called vii on the abdomen. In Saturniidae, e. g. *Samia cecropia* (Fig. 107), each thoracic segment bears a scolus at the base of the leg, and in line with these scoli are found similar ones on abdominal segments 1 and 2. The latter are not present, however, on segments 3 to 6. As usual, vii of the proleg-bearing segments is modified into a multisetiferous plate and not into a thorn-like process. If the scoli on segments 1 and 2 represented the seta "vi" or mu, they would also be found on segments 3 to 6 near the base of the prolegs, as in arctians and other verrucose larvae, for mu never takes part in the formation of a multisetiferous leg-plate. These scoli must then be homotypes of vii. But they are also indisputably homotypic with Pi on the thorax. Therefore Pi and vii are homotypic and vii should be called Pi.

Dyar (1901) interpreted this condition correctly and Quail (1904) agreed with him. The views expressed in this paper are in accordance with those of Quail on all the setae which he studied. A careful interpretation of the evidence must convince one that Pi is homologous with "vii" of the abdomen and has no relation to mu.

Mu. Mu, as has been said, arises at the first molt of Frenatae between eta and the Pi group. Apparently it is homotypic with pi of the metathorax, but its absence from Hepialus, Panorpa, and the first stage of all caterpillars, shows that this is out of the question. What, then, accounts for its presence?

The fact that the prolegs, and consequently the Pi group, on the abdomen are farther mesad than the thoracic legs has been noted. This change, which is barely indicated in the Jugatae, leaves a considerable space between eta and pi on the abdominal segments. Assuming that the setae are sensory in function, it is clear that the presence of a sense organ in this important area would be of selective value. A discussion of the method of origin of new or secondary setae in response to a need on the part of the organism would be out of place here, but that they do arise and are of importance to the life of the caterpillar is shown by the conspicuous differences between the mature larvae of different families. In this case mu appeared in the center of an area left vacant by the mesal migration of the prolegs and the Pi group, and has been retained because it is, like the other sense organs of the larva, an adaptation to the conditions of existence.

Sigma. Near the medioventral line of almost every lepidopterous larva, sigma may be found in nearly the same position on every segment. So far as known it is never associated with other setae except in some groups in which it is drawn into the formation of a multi-setiferous leg-plate.

Tau. The name Tau has been given to an indefinite group of setae between pi and sigma. Various numbers are present, ranging from one to three or four, or the entire group may be absent. So far as known, only one is ever present in the first instar. This is the cephalic or mesal seta of the group of three at the base of the proleg on Frenatae and newly hatched Jugatae. Dyar calls all three the ''tubercle vii'' but a very little study of the first two abdominal segments shows that the two caudolateral members of the group have a distinctly different origin from the other. When four setae are found upon this aspect of the proleg, as in Hepialus, the additional one is considered as another member of the group Tau. In the description of this genus on a previous page the individual setae of the group were named, but that is scarcely necessary in Frenatae.

VI. General Conclusions.

The setal arrangement of every segment of the body in larvae of the Lepidoptera has been derived from the same ancestral type.

This type includes twelve primary setae: alpha, beta, delta, gamma, epsilon, rho, kappa, eta, nu, pi, tau, and sigma.

The primary setae are present in the first instar. They became established before the suborders of Lepidoptera separated from each other and possibly before the separation of the order from other Holometabola. It is not necessary to assume, however, that there ever existed a single insect larva having the setal plan of all the segments similar and including only the primary setae as given above.

The ancestral type has been modified in three ways, each being more or less independent of the other two. *(a)* The prothorax shows a tendency to retain the maximum number of setae; this is a response to the numerous sensory stimuli which this segment must transmit. *(b)* The mesothorax and metathorax show a partial reduction and considerable modification in response to the necessary mobility of this portion of the body. *(c)* The abdominal chaetotaxy has also been reduced but the setae tend to retain their original typical position. Segments 9 and 10 show specialized modifications of the setal arrangement of segments 1 to 8.

Subprimary setae are those which, altho they have a definite location on the mature larva and are rather persistent, are absent from the first instar.

New setae have usually appeared first in that part of the body in which they were of most benefit, e. g., gamma on the prothorax and eta on the abdomen. In some cases setae which seem to be homologous with them have arisen later on other segments. The order of their appearance is now shown in ontogeny.

In addition to the doubtful subprimary homotypes of gamma and eta, there are two rather persistent subprimary setae: theta, which is found on the mesothorax and metathorax of both suborders and on the abdomen of Jugatae; and mu, which is more recent and appears only on the abdomen of Frenatae.

Subprimaries of less common occurrence are omega and phi of the Tau group, while still others are present in certain families.

Primary or primary and subprimary setae tend to associate with each other in groups. These groups are indicated in this paper by capital letters.

The Beta group consists of alpha and beta; Rho, of epsilon and rho; Kappa, of theta, kappa, and eta; Pi, of pi and nu; and Tau, of tau, omega, and phi. On the abdomen tau is associated with the Pi group.

Both primary and subprimary setae may develop into tufts borne on verrucae. The verrucae of the same setal group tend to coalesce, while those of different groups tend to remain distinct.

SYNONYMS

In the following tables are given the names used by various authors for the different setae on the segments heretofore studied. A parenthesis indicates that the seta is subprimary in the region of the body referred to. "O" indicates that the seta is absent from that region; while a dash is used when the author fails to mention the seta.

Mesothorax and Metathorax. (Frenatae)

	Dyar, 1895	Dyar, 1901	Quail, 1904	Forbes, 1910
alpha	i a	i	i	i a
beta	i b	ii	ii	i b
(gamma)	—	—	—	x
delta	o	o	o	o
epsilon	ii a	iii	iii a	ii a
rho	ii b	iv	iii	ii b
(theta)	iii	v a	iv	iii
kappa	iv	v	v	iv
(eta)	v	v b	vi	v
(mu)	o	o	o	o
pi	vi	vi	vii	vii
nu	o	o	o	o
tau	—	—	—	ix
(omega)	—	—	—	—
sigma	viii	—	—	viii

Abdomen

	Müller, 1886 Nymphalidae 1st stage	Dyar, 1895 Frenatae	Dyar, 1901 Frenatae	Quail, 1904 Frenatae	Forbes, 1910 Frenatae	Forbes, 1910 Jugatae
alpha	1	i	i	i	i	i
beta	2	ii	ii	ii	ii	ii
(gamma)	0	—	—	—	x	—
delta	0	o	o	o	o	o
epsilon	—	iii a	—	iii a	iii a	iii a
rho	3	iii	iii	iii	iii	iii
(theta)	0	o	o	o	o	iv
kappa	4	iv	iv	iv.	iv	v
eta	5	v	v	v	v	vi
(mu)	0	vi	v b	vi	vi	o
pi	6	vii	vi	vii	vii	vii
nu	6	vii	vi	vii	vii	vii
tau	—	vii	vi	vii	vii	vii
(omega)	0	—	—	—	ix	ix
sigma	—	viii	—	—	viii	viii

PART TWO. SYSTEMATIC OUTLINE OF
FAMILIES AND GENERA.

A complete history of the study of caterpillars would begin with
work done centuries ago and would include the names of many
scientists. It would necessarily embrace all discussions of larvae of the
Lepidoptera. There is now in manuscript a list, as nearly complete as
such a list can be made, of all published papers containing descriptions
of immature stages of American members of this order, but its size is so
great that arrangements for its publication are difficult. Nevertheless,
no object would be served here by an extended historical account, especially as the results obtained by the older workers were not of such a
nature as to aid materially in the preparation of this paper.

The period from Aristotle to the last quarter of the nineteenth century is discussed at some length in the introduction to "Die Schmetterlinge Europas," the third edition, edited by Arnold Spuler. Since that
time the subject has been put on a more scientific basis by the work of
two men. Dr. Harrison G. Dyar, in addition to the papers mentioned
in Part One, has written excellent descriptions of new larvae for various
publications every year for a quarter of a century. These are undoubtedly the best descriptions of larval Macroheterocera extant, for they give
not only color but the structural characters which indicate their family
and sometimes their generic position. Since 1905 several papers have
been published by Dr. W. T. M. Forbes, who has made a detailed study
of the head sclerites, mouth parts, and prolegs of a large number of
species. Representatives of all the more important families of Macrolepidoptera have been described and figured. The observations of Dyar
and Forbes mark the first advance stride toward an accurate knowledge
of the structure and relationships of the larvae of this order.

In spite of the work of these investigators certain gaps remain in
our knowledge, especially of those species of importance to economic
entomologists. The most conspicuous of these is our ignorance of the
structure and taxonomic characters of the larvae of the Microlepidoptera. It is true, as one author puts it, that "there seems to be little

variation in these forms,'' but the characters are present and their obscurity merely challenges us to closer search. Another demand of economic workers is an analytical key to the families. Dyar's few tables are usually not adapted to the identification of individual specimens, for he uses characters which, in the later stages of many species, are completely obscured by secondary setae or entirely lost. The best key thus far published is that by Forbes (1910), but it omits nearly all the Microlepidoptera as well as the more obscure families of the larger moths and butterflies. There are species he had not seen which trace to families in which they do not belong, but such a fault is one a worker on immature insects is unable to avoid.

In several respects a systematic outline of larvae differs from a classification of a group of imagines. It is clear that while a difference in larval characters indicates a phylogenetic divergence just as surely as does a variation in adult structure, similarity in the adults of a group of genera does not necessarily indicate the presence of common characters in the larvae. One always faces the fact that he is working with genera and families established on adult characters and that the unknown species of a particular group may be very different from those with which he is acquainted.

Another element of doubt is caused by the necessity of breeding. One can not breed a specimen and keep it too. Larvae must always be identified from the adults into which their *associates* develop except when they are raised from fertilized eggs laid by a known female. The danger of mistaken records can be greatly reduced by careful work but when handling large numbers of species can never be wholly eliminated.

It should also be noted that the adult state represents a single instar while the larva undergoes several molts, changing materially at least once. Wherever possible a description should include all the instars. In this paper, only the more mature larvae were considered, as a rule, but in most families the characters used apply to all except the first or the first and second stages. Usually only the colors change after the second molt.

These sources of error were reduced in importance by the confirmation of observations on long series of individuals. The larvae of several large collections were examined, with the result that several mistakes due to these causes were corrected.

CHARACTERS USED

Adult insects are identified mainly on characters of the wings, segmented appendages, body sclerites, copulatory apparatus, and vestiture of the body and legs. Of these, all except the segmented appendages

and vestiture are either absent or indistinguishable in lepidopterous
larvae. The mouth parts and antennae of all but a few species are
constructed on the same plan and show such limited variation that little
use can be made of them. No one has yet discovered characters of much
value in the structure of the thoracic legs, so uniform are they throughout the entire order. The vestiture is also entirely different from that
of other insects. It is consequently necessary to seek other characters
than those with which entomologists are usually familiar and to introduce new terms to describe them.

The structures of value in the classification of these larvae are pri-
marily: the head sclerites, head setae, and ocelli; the armature of the
body, especially the setae; the shape of the spiracles; the number of
prolegs and the arrangement of the crochets they bear; and the presence
on the body of humps and gibbosities, eversible glands, or peculiar modifications of the usual organization. These will be taken up in order.

Head parts.—The varying shapes of the head sclerites and positions
of the setae are so well shown by Forbes (1910) that they need little
attention here. The head capsule consists almost entirely of an epicranium divided into three parts by the forked epicranial suture. These
parts are the right and left sides and the front. The latter is usually
a triangular sclerite on the facial aspect of the head. To its ventral
margin is attached the trapezoidal clypeus which supports the labrum.
Laterad of each arm of the epicranial suture is a narrow area, the adfrontal piece (afp, Fig. 78), the exterior indication of the anterior arm
of the tentorium. In this region the varying sizes and shapes of the
front, the adfrontals, and the labrum, and the location of the setae they
bear, are important characters for identification.

At the point where the caudodorsal part of the head capsule joins
either the prothorax or the unchitinized portion of the head, there is a
pale triangular dorsal area of thin cuticula. The cephalic point of this
triangle in all except a few caterpillars is at the caudal end of the epicranial suture and its sides are formed by the caudad projecting lobes
of the epicranium. This dorsal area is known as the "vertical triangle",
or sometimes merely the "vertex", although the latter term properly
applies to the dorsal part of the head capsule itself. In some leaf-
miners the front extends caudodorsad as far as this triangle and the
arms of the epicranial suture do not unite to form a stem. The front
in such cases is said to be "open". In very small larvae, however, care
must be taken in determining this point, for microscopic preparations
show the tentorial arms much more distinctly than the epicranial suture,
and these internal arms usually do not meet on the vertex. The
head setae are numbered according to Dyar's scheme (Figs. 78, 86).

As the head is not a single metamere we can not homologize these setae with those of the body segments.

The ocelli seem to form one of the most satisfactory characters for the separation of genera. In most families their arrangement and the position of the setae associated with them are constant in long series of individuals and species. Without their aid the difficulties in the classification of some of the Microlepidoptera would be almost insurmountable. The dorsal four usually form the quadrant of a circle, with the other two below them and farther apart. (Figs. 70, 71.) Beginning at the caudal ocellus of the dorsal group we may call them the first to the fourth in regular order. The fifth is caudoventrad of the fourth and in some cases farther ventrad than the sixth (Fig. 77) which is the one most cephalic in position.

Armature of the body.—In Part One it was shown that lepidopterous larvae have certain setae in a definite arrangement. These were denominated by Greek letters and their homotypy was studied in order that any particular letter might be made to apply to the same or homotypic setae on every segment of every caterpillar. For that study it was necessary to distinguish between primary and subprimary setae, the latter being missing from the first instar. In classification, however, this distinction is rarely of any value, and as subprimaries are few in number the normal ones are assumed to be present in all mature larvae. A statement in a description that a mature larva bears primary setae only, is to be interpreted on this basis.

The more conspicuous forms of armature are usually associated with groups of setae. "Tubercles", "warts", and "spines" are terms now in use describing them. The first has the disadvantage of meaning any cuticular projection of the body wall from a minute papilla to a conspicuous prominence. "Spines" have also been used both for the projections of the body wall and for the branches of any thorn-like process. A number of new terms are therefore suggested for particular kinds of armature. Their derivation is given except where it will be perfectly evident.

In the most generalized larvae a seta is surrounded at the base by a small chitinized ring, very slightly raised. This ring may be called a *papilla,* following Scudder. It is often surrounded by a small and definitely bounded chitinized area or *pinaculum* (L. *pinax,* dim., "a small plate"), such as is seen in many Microlepidoptera (Figs. 15, 40). When the pinaculum is conspicuously elevated at the center and bears the seta on a distinct projection, it may be termed a *chalaza* (Gr. χαλαζα, "pimple", or "tubercle"), as in the arctian Utetheisa (Fig. 90). Either the pinaculum or the chalaza may be double or triple, and may accordingly bear two or three setae (K, fig. 39) ; but neither is ever multisetiferous.

When the setae are increased in number new modifications are to be noted in the cuticular areas to which they are attached. The most common tendency is toward the development of tufts, in which case each tuft is said to be borne on a *verruca* (L. *verruca,* "wart") as shown in Fig. 88. If the setae are so thickly grouped as to form a dense upright bundle, the term *verricule* (Fig. 91), already in use in entomology, describes their condition. In some cases the setae are increased in number on a pinaculum without forming tufts, as on the prolegs of notodontians and arctians (Fig. 100). As the term *plate* is already in use for this structure and is not applied to other different conditions, it is adopted here.

More conspicuous than verrucae are the thorny processes bearing spine-like setae, found in saturnian and nymphalid larvae (Fig. 74), and for them the term *scolus* (Gr. κολ ος, "thorn") is particularly appropriate. When the setae are borne on sharp lateral projections of the scolus, these projections are known as *spinules.*

As the word *tubercle* has been applied to each one of the above structures by previous writers, it is deemed best to retain it as a general term.

Spiracles.—A classification of larvae based on the spiracles is still unwritten. It is to be hoped that some future investigator will study their structure and report the variations in different families. As yet little use can be made of them altho differences in their shape, location, and formation can not but be noted. One case in which they are useful is the pyrali-zygaenoid series in which the spiracles become smaller and smaller as the insects become more and more specialized. Certain of these families, such as the Pyromorphidae, can not be easily distinguished from some Bombycoidea by the arrangement of their verrucae, but their small, circular spiracles are very different. (Figs. 79, 104.)

Prolegs.—Nearly two hundred years ago Reaumur figured four or five forms of prolegs and the hooks attached to them. He made no use of them in classification but the figures are more accurately drawn than those of most later workers. Chapman was the first to call attention to the fact that the crochets of Microlepidoptera are usually arranged in a circle while those of the Macros are, in most cases, placed in a single longitudinal row.

Prolegs are normally present on segments 3, 4, 5, 6, and 10 of the abdomen, one pair to each segment. In general statements only the first four pairs are referred to. When it seems necessary to distinguish these specifically from the last pair, those of segment 10 are known as the *anal* prolegs and the others as the *ventral*.

The tip of the proleg on which the hooks or crochets are borne is called the planta. In the most generalized forms (e. g. Pseudanaphora, Hepialus) this planta bears a complete circle of well developed crochets surrounded by several more circles of smaller ones. In Hepialus the differences between the inner and outer are not as marked as in Pseudanaphora (Fig. 96). This arrangement is a *multiserial circle* and is confined to Hepialidae, Acrolophidae, and Yponomeutidae. From it the crochets may be lost in the mesal and lateral parts of the circle as in Adela (Fig. 94), resulting in two *transverse multiserial bands,* which degenerate in Incurvaria to a single transverse uniserial band. Where the outer circles entirely disappear the resulting condition is known as a *uniserial circle* (Fig. 101), for the crochets are in a single, continuous series.

The uniserial circle has the bases of all the crochets in line but the lengths are seldom uniform. We are able to distinguish *uniordinal* crochets (Fig. 105), in which the tips as well as the bases are in a straight line, from the *biordinal* (Fig. 106), in which the crochets are of two distinct lengths alternating. Occasionally *triordinal* crochets (Fig. 98) are seen, but Forbes's separation of Rhopalocera from Heterocera on this basis fails to be confirmed by observation. In fact the irregularities in the lengths of the biordinal crochets make any extensive use of the difference in the number of sizes inadvisable. On the other hand the uniordinal series is usually definite, and the irregularities, except at the ends of the row, are negligible.

Having a complete uniserial circle of crochets, a group may develop *transverse bands* (Fig. 99) by the loss of both the mesal and lateral parts of the circle, or a *penellipse* (L. *paene*+*ellipsis*, ''almost an ellipse'') by the loss of only a short portion on one side. The penellipse may be *lateral* as in Psychidae (Fig. 85), where the gap in the series is near the meson; or it may be *mesal* as in Pyraustinae (Fig. 98), where the lost crochets were farthest from the meson.

Finally more than half the circle may be lost and a *mesoseries* (Fig. 105) result. This is the arrangement seen in nearly all the Macrolepidoptera except Hesperoidea. In certain families a few rudimentary hooks remain (or are secondarily developed) on the lateral portion of the planta. As there is no case in which these even approach the size of the mesal crochets there is no likelihood of this condition, to which the term *pseudocircle* (Fig. 97) may be applied, being confused with a circle or penellipse.

The crochets of a mesoseries, penellipse, or circle may be either uniordinal or biordinal, as described above. In addition, arctians and a few other families show a peculiar specialization. The planta (Fig. 100) is longitudinally extended beyond the series of well developed crochets, which in these cases are always uniordinal. At each end of this planta is a row of much smaller chitinous processes, usually not hooked. These are often so slightly developed that they are difficult to demonstrate, but the type of arrangement is easily made out by the short row of crochets on the elongated planta. We may apply to this condition the term *heteroideous* (Fig. 100) now used by botanists for "diversified in form". In distinction from this, crochets of the ordinary mesoseries are called *homoideous* (Fig. 105).

Modifications, not well covered by the above terms, are found in Megalopygidae and Lycaenidae. In the former the mesoseries makes a sharp angle cephalad of the middle while the crochets near the angle are as short as those at the ends of the series. The genus Carama has a distinct gap at the angle so that the hooks are in two groups. In some Lycaenidae (Fig. 102) there is a similar gap near the middle of the series and from the planta at this point arises a small fleshy protuberance. The latter is present in all members of the family altho in many genera the crochets are merely shortened opposite it instead of being wanting.

Other structures.—Certain genera and families show peculiar specializations which are of value in identification. The most common of these are eversible glands, or osmateria, such as are used in distinguishing Papilionidae, Parnassiidae, and Liparidae. The dorsal gland on the seventh abdominal segment of Lycaenidae is also said to occur in all species but is so minute that it is usually overlooked. The ventral prothoracic glands of many noctuids, notodontians, and nymphalids are conspicuous enough but their occurrence does not usually depend upon family or generic limits.

Several kinds of processes of the body wall are less closely associated with setae than are scoli and verrucae. The most common of these are *cornicula*, or little horns, usually heavily chitinized. They are very often present on the suranal plate. A corniculum is similar to a chalaza in shape but does not bear a seta.

Certain slender fleshy processes have been given the name, "fleshy filaments", by former authors, and that term describes their structure so well that no further explanation is necessary. They vary from one to many pairs and are found in all Lymnadidae (Fig. 92) and in the papilionid genus Laertias.

Other projections of the body wall are described in connection with the larvae which bear them. *Gibbosities* are large round dorsal swellings more like malformations than processes. *Horns* are sharp pointed and unbranched, the caudal horn of the sphingids being the best example. *Protuberances* are large rounded swellings without definite outlines and are usually lateral in position.

There are two or more large chitinized plates covering the dorsal half of a segment. The first is the prothoracic shield (Figs. 7, 25, etc.), a thickening of the cuticula covering the greater part of the dorsal half of the prothorax. In a few cases shields are also developed on segments II and 9. The dorsum of segment 10 bears the suranal plate, which varies from a mere thickening of the body wall to a highly modified and variously specialized structure. (Fig. 84.)

A glossary giving all these terms will be found at the close of the paper. Following it, the method of numbering the segments is described and a list of the Greek letters used for setae is given.

CLASSIFICATION

In nomenclature Dyar's "List of North American Lepidoptera" (1902) has been followed throughout. While this list is not perfect, it is widely distributed and is the most accurate one now extant. In a few cases in which the genus has been divided since the publication of that list the new names are used but the old ones are included in parenthesis. Certain species have also been described since 1902 and they are the only ones for which the authority is given. Outside the Microlepidoptera, the only important change in the families is in the transference of Apatelodes from Notodontidae to Eupterotidae and in the rearrangement of the Saturnioidea.

It has been necessary to revise the Microlepidoptera entirely, owing to a rapid advance in our knowledge of the adults. The grouping and the division into families is principally a compilation from Walsingham and from published and unpublished work of August Busck. At the same time we believe that nothing in the larval structure precludes this arrangement and that it is a more natural classification than any published more than a decade ago.

The order of treatment is the reverse of that usually followed in Lepidoptera. There seems to be no excuse for beginning lists and outlines of this order with the most specialized forms when a treatment of Hymenoptera always starts with a consideration of the Tenthredinoidea, Coleoptera with the Carabidae, Diptera with the Nematocera, etc. The latter arrangement is the logical one and the most natural. For that reason families are listed here in an order which proceeds so far as possible from generalized to specialized. In most cases, consequently, it is the exact reverse of that followed in Dyar's List.

FAMILIES OF LEPIDOPTERA

a. Thoracic legs wanting or mere fleshy swellings.
  b. Body fleshy and swollen at middle, fusiform; front closed above.
                                                    PRODOXIDAE
  bb. Body cylindrical or depressed, never fusiform.
    c. Head with ocelli of each side either six in number or reduced to
      one; front reaching vertical triangle.
      d. Head with all ocelli small, subequal in size.
        e. Abdominal segments 3, 4, 5, and 6 with rudimentary prolegs,
          each bearing several transverse bands of crochets.
                                                    TISCHERIIDAE
        ee. Abdomen either without prolegs or crochets or with crochets
          on segments 3, 4, and 5.   GRACILARIIDAE
      dd. Head with one large and conspicuous ocellus on each side.
        e. Ocelli cephalic, located close to lateral angles of clypeus;
          front triangular in outline.   MICROPTERYGIDAE
        ee. Ocelli lateral, distant from lateral angles of clypeus; front
          quadrangular.
          f. Front wider at caudal end than at cephalic; body often de-
            pressed and moniliform; prolegs not as in the alterna-
            tive.   GRACILARIIDAE
          ff. Front narrower at caudal end than at cephalic; body
            always cylindrical; segments II and III and 2 to 7 bear-
            ing prolegs without crochets (Fig. 93).
                                                    NEPTICULIDAE
    cc. Head with two conspicuous ocelli on each side; front not reach-
      ing vertex.   HELIODINIDAE
aa. Thoracic legs present and segmented.
  b. Prolegs and crochets wholly wanting.
    c. Body fusiform; head small but not greatly depressed; front not
      extending to vertical triangle.
      d. Intersegmental incisions indistinct; scoli usually present; body
        colored; size large.   COCHLIDIIDAE
      dd. Intersegmental incisions distinct; scoli never present; body
        pale; size very small.
        e. Kappa and eta distant or all setae wanting. PRODOXIDAE
        ee. Kappa and eta adjacent; setae small but distinct.
                                                    GELECHIIDAE
    cc. Body usually cylindrical, always very small; head depressed
      but not narrowed; front extending to vertical triangle.
                                                    COLEOPHORIDAE

bb. Prolegs always present, when reduced represented by at least rudimentary crochets.

　c. Body bearing neither tufted nor secondary setae; prolegs not bearing more than four setae (pi, nu, tau, and sigma) (Fig. 101), except that there may be five when crochets are arranged in a multiserial circle; mu never a verruca, never associated with additional subprimaries.

　　d. Crochets never arranged in a pseudocircle (Fig. 97) or meso-series (Fig. 105), usually in a circle (Fig. 101) or penellipse (Fig. 98) or transverse bands (Fig. 99); epsilon on prothorax always below alpha and gamma (Fig. 7).

　　　e. Prolegs of sixth abdominal segment absent or without cro-chets; larvae small, leaf-miners.   GRACILARIIDAE

　　　ee. Prolegs of sixth abdominal segment as well developed as those of segments 3, 4, and 5.

　　　　f. Kappa group on prothorax bisetose, theta absent (Fig. 43); crochets never multiserial.

　　　　　g. Crochets uniordinal, arranged in a complete circle; body cylindrical; Pi group on mesothorax unisetose.   ORNEODIDAE

　　　　　gg. Crochets biordinal (Figs. 98, 101), except when body is spindle-shaped and very fleshy and when Pi group on mesothorax is bisetose (Fig. 50).   PYRALIDIDAE

　　　　ff. Kappa group on prothorax trisetose, theta present (Fig. 39).

　　　　　g. Crochets arranged in transverse bands (Fig. 99).

　　　　　　h. Crochets arranged either in a single transverse row or in two multiserial bands on each proleg.   INCURVARIIDAE

　　　　　　hh. Crochets always arranged in two uniserial bands on each proleg.

　　　　　　　i. Kappa and eta of abdomen remote.   BUCCULATRIGIDAE

　　　　　　　ii. Kappa and eta of abdomen adjacent (Fig. 41).

　　　　　　　　j. Crochets of anal prolegs in two groups.   GELECHIIDAE

　　　　　　　　jj. Crochets of anal prolegs in a single transverse row.

　　　　　　　　　k. Front extending about one third of the distance to the vertical triangle.   COSSIDAE

　　　　　　　　　kk. Front extending at least two thirds of the dis-tance to the vertical triangle.

l. Spiracles elliptical, normal in size, those of
segment 8 farther dorsad than others.
AEGERIIDAE

ll. Spiracles circular, very small, the pair of
segment 8 about in line; crochets of right
and left sides usually almost continuous
across ventromeson.   COLEOPHORIDAE

gg. Crochets arranged in a circle or penellipse.

h. Kappa and eta of abdomen remote or eta wanting
(Fig. 8).

i. Crochets arranged in a multiserial circle (Fig. 96)
or in a penellipse (Fig. 98).

j. Setae beta of prothorax closer together on dorsum
than setae alpha; crochets always in a multiserial circle.   ACROLOPHIDAE

jj. Setae beta on prothorax farther apart than setae
alpha.

k. Theta absent on abdomen (Fig. 37); beta,
delta, and rho distant on the prothorax (Fig.
35); crochets sometimes in a penellipse.
YPONOMEUTIDAE

kk. Theta present on abdomen (Fig. 6); beta,
delta, and rho adjacent on prothorax (Fig. 5).
HEPIALIDAE

ii. Crochets arranged in a uniserial circle.

j. Prothorax with setae of Kappa group distant,
about as far from spiracle as from each other;
setae alpha of abdomen closer together than
setae beta.   LYONETIIDAE

jj. Prothorax with setae of Kappa group all close
together, twice as far from spiracle as from
each other.

k. Setae alpha of abdomen much farther apart on
dorsum than setae beta.   TINEIDAE

kk. Setae alpha of abdomen not farther apart on
dorsum than setae beta.   HELIODINIDAE

hh. Kappa and eta of abdomen adjacent (Fig. 41); crochets in a uniserial circle or penellipse.

i. Pi group of mesothorax bisetose (Fig. 36).

j. Long axis of prothoracic spiracle vertical; setae
alpha of segment 9 closer together than setae
beta.   THYRIDIDAE

jj. Long axis of prothoracic spiracle horizontal
(Fig. 69).   PSYCHIDAE

ii. Pi group on mesothorax unisetose (Fig. 40); setae
alpha of segment 9 farther apart than setae beta.

j. Setae beta closer together on segment 9 than on
any other abdominal segment, usually on the
same or adjacent pinacula (Fig. 42).

TORTRICIDAE

jj. Setae beta at least as far apart on segment 9
as on other abdominal segments, never borne
on the same or adjacent pinacula (Fig. 56).

k. Mandibles large and conspicuous, extending far
beyond margins of labrum (Fig. 72); larvae
borers, in later instars very large.

COSSIDAE

kk. Mandibles small, larvae leaf-feeders, always
small.

l. Coxae of metathoracic legs twice as far apart
as wide; setae indistinct, prolegs small.

COSMOPTERYGIDAE

ll. Coxae of metathoracic legs never twice as far
apart as wide.

m. Adfrontals reaching vertical triangle or
nearly so; front extending two thirds
of the distance to the vertical triangle,
when shorter forming an attenuate point,
or head not depressed, not held horizontally.

n. Crochets biordinal in most species; ad-
domen with alpha and beta remote,
segment 8 with rho never caudodorsad
of spiracle.

o. Fourth ocellus much closer to third
than to sixth, second closer to third
than to first.   OECOPHORIDAE*

oo. Third ocellus not so closely associated
with second and fourth.

GELECHIIDAE*

nn. Crochets uniordinal.

---

*Characters separating these two families and the next not constant.

o. Abdomen with rho of segment 8 caudodorsad of spiracle, alpha and beta
remote.   BLASTOBASIDAE*

oo. Abdomen with rho of segment 8 dorsad or cephalodorsad of spiracle.

p. Alpha and beta of abdomen adjacent. (Schreckensteinia).
YPONOMEUTIDAE

pp. Alpha and beta of abdomen remote.   HEMEROPHILIDAE

mm. Adfrontals reaching about two thirds,
front less than half, the distance to vertical triangle; front blunt at apex; head
depressed, held horizontally.
STENOMIDAE

dd. Crochets arranged in a pseudocircle (Fig. 97) or mesoseries
(Figs. 100, 105).

e. Prothorax with Kappa group trisetose, and with epsilon below alpha and gamma, not near rho (Fig. 35).

f. Kappa and eta of abdomen remote; crochets uniordinal,
sometimes arranged in a pseudocircle.
YPONOMEUTIDAE

ff. Kappa and eta of abdomen adjacent; crochets arranged in
a mesoseries.

g. Setae beta of prothorax about as far apart as setae
alpha; prolegs usually short.   ETHMIIDAE

gg. Setae beta of prothorax very much closer together than
setae alpha; prolegs long and slender.
HEMEROPHILIDAE

ee. Prothorax with Kappa group bisetose, and with epsilon associated with rho between delta and spiracle (Fig. 21); kappa
and eta of abdomen remote; crochets arranged in a mesoseries, usually uniordinal.

f. Pi group on mesothorax and metathorax bisetose (Fig. 50).

g. Setae small, borne on minute papillae. THYATIRIDAE

gg. Setae well developed, borne on chalazae.

h. Chalazae rho of abdominal segments bisetose.
LITHOSIIDAE

hh. Chalazae rho of abdomen unisetose (Utetheisa).
ARCTIIDAE

---

*Characters separating this and the two preceding families not constant.

ff. Pi group on mesothorax and metathorax unisetose (Fig. 22).

   g. Body without conspicuous gibbosities.   NOCTUIDAE

   gg. Body with one or more distinct transverse dorsal gibbosities; coloration mainly in transverse stripes.

$$\left\{\begin{array}{l}\text{AGARISTIDAE}\\\text{NOCTUIDAE}\end{array}\right.$$

cc. Body bearing tufted or secondary setae or at least five setae on prolegs; mu usually associated with several other subprimaries (Figs. 59 to 68); crochets never arranged in a multiserial circle.

  d. Crochets uniordinal (Figs. 100, 105).

    e. Number of pairs of ventral prolegs three or six.

      f. Abdominal segments 2 to 7, inclusive, bearing prolegs, those of segments 2 and 7 without crochets; verrucae bearing large numbers of fine setae.

          MEGALOPYGIDAE

      ff. Abdominal segments 2, 3 and 7 not bearing prolegs; verrucae bearing few setae.   NOLIDAE

    ee. Number of pairs of ventral prolegs four.

      f. Verrucae reduced, or obscured by development of secondary setae, or absent.

        g. Head muricate; ocelli on papillae, the third very large.

          AGAPETIDAE

        gg. Head smooth or nearly so; ocelli sessile, the third normal.

          h. Body very small, hemispherical in shape; head retractile, minute; habit parasitic; crochets uniordinal, arranged in a complete circle.   EPIPYROPIDAE

        hh. Body cylindrical; habits not parasitic.

          i. Secondary setae numerous, often obscuring both primary setae and verrucae.

            j. Spiracles small, circular (Fig. 104); ventral prolegs long, slender (Fig. 95).

              PTEROPHORIDAE

            jj. Spiracles elliptical, well developed (Fig. 79); ventral prolegs short (Fig. 105).

              k. Notch of labrum deep, with parallel sides and rounded bottom (see footnote, p. —); body often bearing tufts and pencils of setae but never with cornicula.   NOCTUIDAE

              kk. Notch of labrum acute, not with parallel sides; body never bearing tufts and pencils of setae but sometimes with cornicula.

NOTODONTIDAE

ii. Secondary setae absent or sparse; primary setae
always distinct, tho sometimes small.

j. Kappa at about the same level on abdominal segments 6, 7, and 8; setae very small; no
humps, horns, or minute cuticular processes
present. (Doa).   ARCTIIDAE

jj. Kappa much lower on segment 7 than on segments 6 and 8 (Fig. 31).

k. Suranal plate terminating in an acute process
and anal prolegs wanting (Fig. 89); crochets
in a pseudocircle (Fig. 97).

PLATYPTERYGIDAE

kk. Suranal plate rounded posteriorly; crochets
in a mesoseries.

l. Body covered with minute cuticular processes; form cylindrical except for a dorsal gibbosity on abdominal segment 8; no
stemapoda or horns present.

DIOPTIDAE

ll. Body not covered with minute processes;
horns, stemapoda, or gibbosities usually
present.   NOTODONTIDAE

ff. Verrucae (Fig. 88), at least mu, well developed, distinct,
bearing many setae; secondary setae sparse or absent except on prolegs.

g. Eversible mediodorsal glands present on abdominal segments 6 and 7.   LIPARIDAE

gg. Eversible dorsal glands wanting.

h. Spiracles large, elliptical (Fig. 79).

i. Verruca kappa in about the same position on abdominal segment 7 as on segments 6 and 8 (Figs.
33, 67, 68); when somewhat lower, mesothorax
bearing only one verruca above the Kappa group.

j. Mesothorax bearing only one verruca above Kappa
group on each side.   SYNTOMIDAE

jj. Mesothorax bearing two verrucae above Kappa
group on each side (Fig. 26).   ARCTIIDAE

ii. Verruca kappa much lower in position on segment
7 than on segments 6 and 8, often absent or fused
with verruca eta especially on segment 7 (Figs.
65, 66).

j. Crochets homoideous (Fig. 105); mesothorax
     bearing two verrucae above Kappa group; lab-
     rum with a deep, parallel-sided notch.
                                        NOCTUIDAE

jj. Crochets heteroideous (Fig. 100); mesothorax
     usually bearing only one verruca above Kappa
     group; verrucae conspicuous, altho without nu-
     merous setae.   PERICOPIDAE

hh. Spiracles small, circular (Fig. 104).
     i. Head small, retractile; prolegs short.
                                     PYROMORPHIDAE

     ii. Head not retractile; prolegs long, slender, cylin-
          drical (Fig. 95).   PTEROPHORIDAE

dd. Crochets biordinal or triordinal (Figs. 102, 106).
  e. Setae of body either primary or tufted, never numerous and
     secondary; several subprimaries present on venter or on
     prolegs, sometimes rather numerous when anal prolegs are
     wanting or ventral prolegs reduced in number (Fig. 63).
  f. Crochets in a complete circle (Fig. 101).
     g. Alpha and beta of abdomen in the form of verrucae.
          (Scythris).   YPONOMEUTIDAE

     gg. Alpha and beta of abdomen single setae; kappa and
          eta of abdomen adjacent.   LACOSOMIDAE

  ff. Crochets in a mesoseries (Fig. 106) or pseudocircle (Fig.
     97).
     g. Suranal plate terminating in an acute process and anal
          prolegs wanting (Fig. 89); crochets in a pseudocircle.
                                     PLATYPTERYGIDAE

     gg. Suranal plate rounded caudad; anal prolegs present.
       h. Number of pairs of ventral prolegs four, all well
          developed.
          i. Kappa group on prothorax trisetose (Fig. 39);
               kappa and eta of abdomen adjacent.
                                          ETHMIIDAE

          ii. Kappa group on prothorax bisetose (Fig. 43);
               kappa and eta distant, at least on abdominal seg-
               ments 4 to 8.
               j. Prothorax and abdominal segment 8 with spira-
                    cles twice as large as those of other segments.
                                          EPIPLEMIDAE

jj. Prothorax and abdominal segment 8 with spiracles no larger than those of other segments.
THYATIRIDAE

hh. Number of pairs of ventral prolegs reduced, cephalic three pairs rudimentary or wanting.
GEOMETRIDAE

ee. Setae of body secondary, always numerous at least on prolegs; anal pair and four ventral pairs of prolegs always present.

f. Secondary setae very irregular in length, very long setae mixed with others a tenth as long; neither distinct verrucae nor scoli ever present; body often bearing lateroventral, blunt, fleshy protuberances.

g. Labrum deeply notched, notch acute, either reaching over two-thirds the length of the labrum or continued as a groove which reaches clypeus; several mediodorsal pencils of setae often present.   EUPTEROTIDAE

gg. Labrum obtusely notched; notch variable but never reaching two-thirds distance to base of labrum, never continued as a groove which reaches clypeus.
LASIOCAMPIDAE

ff. Secondary setae usually short and uniform in length; when long and irregular either distinct verrucae or scoli are present.

g. Body usually armed with a mediodorsal horn, scar, scolus, or pair of scoli on segment 8; if not, head produced into a high conical point; scoli never present on head nor on dorsomeson of segments 1 to 7; head smooth; crochets usually only biordinal.

h. Body sphingiform, never bearing even rudimentary scoli or secondary setae above level of prolegs.

i. Segments divided into six to eight annulets; prolegs not widely separated.   SPHINGIDAE

ii. Segments not divided into annulets; prolegs widely separated.   BOMBYCIDAE

hh. Body not sphingiform, always bearing at least rudimentary scoli.   SATURNIOIDEA

gg. Body usually not armed with a mediodorsal horn, scar, scolus or pair of scoli on segment 8; when so armed, either segments 4 to 7 also bear unpaired mediodorsal scoli or the head is conspicuously bigibbous above, usually bearing a pair of scoli or pointed prominences; crochets usually triordinal.

h. Crochets arranged in a circle, usually triordinal, lateral crochets about as well developed as mesal; secondary setae small or absent on dorsal half of body, never long and never borne on scoli.

i. Head much larger than prothorax; body largest at middle distinctly tapering toward both ends.

HESPERIIDAE

ii. Head partially retractile, smaller than prothorax; body cylindrical.   MEGATHYMIDAE

hh. Crochets arranged in a mesoseries or pseudocircle, lateral crochets, when present, rudimentary; long setae and scoli sometimes present.

i. Prolegs with mesoseries interrupted or reduced at middle and with a narrow spatulate fleshy lobe arising near the interruption (Fig. 102); head small.

j. Head about half the diameter of the body.

RIODINIDAE

jj. Head usually less than half the diameter of the body.   LYCAENIDAE

ii. Prolegs without a fleshy lobe near the middle of the mesoseries.

j. Osmaterium wanting.

k. Scoli (Figs. 73, 74) or fleshy filaments (Fig. 92) well developed and conspicuous on body; when reduced, large scoli present on head.

l. Mesothorax and sometimes a few other segments bearing fleshy filaments; secondary setae short and confined to prolegs.

LYMNADIDAE

ll. Fleshy filaments never present.

m. Scoli at least twelve times as long as wide, those of abdomen as long as metathorax is wide; each abdominal segment bearing three scoli on each side, none on dorsomeson.   HELICONIIDAE

mm. Scoli when present not so slender; those of abdomen not as long as metathorax is wide; mediodorsal scoli usually present.

NYMPHALIDAE

kk. Scoli never present on head or body; fleshy
  filaments never present.
  l. Suranal plate bifurcate at tip, bearing two
    distinct processes (Fig. 84).
                              AGAPETIDAE
  ll. Suranal plate rounded, entire.
    m. Crochets in a pseudocircle (Fig. 97) ; se-
      tae never borne on chalazae; head small.
                              LIBYTHEIDAE
    mm. Crochets in a mesoseries.
      n. Head conspicuously larger than protho-
        rax.   NYMPHALIDAE
      nn. Head not larger than prothorax; setae
        usually borne on chalazae.
                              PIERIDAE
jj. Osmaterium present on prothorax; when retracted,
  presence shown by dorsal groove through which
  it is everted.
  k. Setae minute, never borne on verrucae except in
    early instars.   PAPILIONIDAE
  kk. Setae well developed; some verrucae present.
                              PARNASSIIDAE

SUBORDER JUGATAE

SUPERFAMILY MICROPTERYGOIDEA

The association of the Hepialidae with the Micropterygidae dates from Comstock's work on wing venation in 1893. Since that time they have usually been placed together in a separate suborder from all other moths and butterflies. There seem to be no larval structures, however, which unite the two families. Dyar (1895b) after studying both Micropteryx and Eriocephala, as well as Hepialus, concludes that, "there is nothing to contradict placing Micropteryx with Hepialus in the suborder Jugatae" and that "there seems to be nothing to preclude a derivation of Eriocephala from Micropteryx"; but these statements are hardly definite enough to convince one of the relationships of the genera in the absence of constructive evidence.

FAMILY HEPIALIDAE

The larvae of several European species of Hepialus will be found described in Part One. (See Figs. 2-6, 13, 14.) In addition it should be mentioned here that the ocelli are not in a semicircle but are in two vertical rows of three each and that the crochets of the ventral prolegs are in a complete multiserial circle, while those of the anal pair are similar but are nearly or quite interrupted caudally. Sthenopis is another American genus of this family but no larvae have been seen by the writer.

FAMILY MICROPTERYGIDAE

The larvae of only one species of this family have been examined. The setae are almost or entirely indistinguishable. Thoracic and abdominal legs are wholly wanting and the head is strongly depressed. The body is thickest at the prothorax and gradually diminishes posteriorly, the anal segment having a very small diameter. The front extends to the large vertical triangle. Close to the cephalic end of each arm of the epicranial suture is a single large ocellus.

Epimartyria auricrinella was the species seen.

SUBORDER FRENATAE

MICROLEPIDOPTERA

Altho much abused, the term Microlepidoptera is a convenient one to indicate the smaller members of the Heterocera. The limits of the group are not now and never can be fixed, for the division is not an entirely natural one. Used here to cover the same families that Dyar's List includes in ''TINEOIDEA'', it embraces three or more wholly separate groups, no more closely related to each other than some of them are to the Macrolepidoptera.

The following is an outline of the classification used in this paper. The sources from which it was drawn and the reasons for departing from Dyar's arrangement are given in the introduction to Part Two. It is followed by a brief discussion of the larval characters which bear on the relationships of the group.

A. Aculeata
Nepticulidae
Prodoxidae
Incurvariidae
Tischeriidae

B. Non-aculeata
a. Tineoid series
Tineoidea
Acrolophidae
Tineidae
Bucculatrigidae
Lyonetiidae
Yponomeutoidea
Heliodinidae
Yponomeutidae
Gracilariidae
Tortricidae
Thyrididae
Aegeriidae
Cossidae

Psychidae
Elachistidae
Coleophoridae
Gelechioidea
    Ethmiidae
    Stenomidae
    Hemerophilidae
    Gelechiidae
    Oecophoridae
    Blastobasidae
    Cosmopterygidae

b. Pyrali-zygaenoid series
    Pyralidoidea
        Pyralididae
        Orneodidae
        Pterophoridae
    Zygaenoidea
        Chalcosidae
        Pyromorphidae
        Epipyropidae
        Dalceridae
        Megalopygidae
        Cochlidiidae

Position uncertain
    Lacosomidae
    Nolidae

Aculeata. The four small families included here are so reduced in size and structure that a classification of them based on larvae would require special preparation and a special set of characters. It is probable that the tentorium will be found to yield important evidence on the relationships of the families to each other and to other leaf-miners, such as the Gracilariidae. In all the species the crochets are wanting or in rudimentary transverse bands. The arrangement of the setae seems in most cases to be indistinguishable. The group Aculeata is based, as yet, wholly on adult structure. While both adults and larvae are specialized by reduction, the presence of aculei, on which the group is based, is a generalized character. The larval structure of the various species is described on a later page.

Non-aculeata. This general term comprises all micros without aculei on the wings. On the basis of larval structure scarcely a single character unites them to each other. The most constant distinctions are in the chaetotaxy of the prothorax. On Pseudanaphora, as on Hepialus, the setae rho and epsilon are as far apart as alpha and beta or nearly so. In Aegeriidae, many Tortricidae and others, rho has migrated forward and has become associated with epsilon below alpha and gamma. One or the other of these two conditions is present in all the Micros. In Macrolepidoptera, on the other hand, epsilon has retreated caudad while rho retains its primitive position below beta and delta. This character, so far as I know, has no exceptions in those forms which bear primary setae only.

A definite and clear distinction is also found in the Kappa group in front of the prothoracic spiracle. In the Macros this group consists of two setae, kappa and eta, while all Micros except Pyralidoidea and Zygaenoidea have three, theta being added.

The crochets also furnish useful characters, varying greatly in the more generalized half of the order but being nearly always arranged in a mesoseries or pseudocircle in the more specialized moths and butterflies. Again the Zygaenoidea must be excepted.

A point to which Dyar called attention twenty years ago is the close relation of kappa and eta ("iv" and "v") on the abdomen and this comes close to covering the Microlepidoptera as here limited. But apparently this was not the generalized condition at all. Nearly all Lepidoptera have descended from species which would now be included in the families Hepialidae, Micropterygidae, Acrolophidae, Tineidae, and Yponomeutidae, and yet all these families have kappa and eta separated, much as in Noctuidae.

The following seems to be the best explanation of the conflicting characters mentioned above:

The setae of the ancestor of all Non-aculeata were arranged very much as in Tineidae and Acrolophidae. (Figs. 7, 8, 15, 16.) Kappa on the prothorax was a trisetose group, epsilon was located below alpha and gamma and not associated with rho, kappa and eta on the abdomen were wholly distinct, and the crochets were in a complete circle, probably multiserial. Gradually evolution of this arrangement resulted in three main divisions, of which it is now impossible to tell which is the oldest.

One of these divisions (Figs. 39-42) retained theta on the prothorax, but, above the most generalized forms, kappa and eta became associated on the abdomen and all sorts of modifications took place in the development of crochets. In these forms epsilon keeps its original position while rho is likely to be found in any location back of it. The members of the Tineoid series possess this variable set of characters and are often honored with the name of "true Micros" in contradistinction to the pyralids and zygaenids.

A second group (Figs. 43-46) was distinguished by the loss of theta on the prothorax and the association of kappa and eta on the abdomen while epsilon remained below alpha and gamma on the prothorax and the crochets remained in a complete circle. The Pyralidoidea and probably the Zygaenoidea have originated from these forms and have retained all three distinctive characters except that the crochets have gradually been reduced in number and groups of adjacent setae have been modified into tufts.

In the third primary division (Figs. 21-24 et al.), theta was lost on the prothorax and epsilon migrated back to rho to cover the opening, kappa and eta remained distant on the abdomen, and the crochets became so limited in number as to reach less than half way round the proleg, forming a mesoseries. From this division have arisen all the true Macroheterocera, i. e., all the Macrolepidoptera except the Rhopalocera.

FAMILY NEPTICULIDAE

The immense number of species in the genus Nepticula causes one to hesitate to make generalizations concerning the family. Many of the larvae have been seen by entomologists, but very few species are familiar to the writer. Descriptions in most cases neglect to state whether legs are present on the thorax or crochets on the abdomen, whether the body is moniliform, depressed or cylindrical, and what is the shape of the front, altho they seldom fail to report whether the body is white or greenish white and that the head is brown.

In all the species of Nepticula examined, and in those described by Wood (1894), both crochets and segmented thoracic legs are wanting; there are two pairs of fleshy leglike swellings on the thoracic segments and six pairs on the abdomen (Fig. 93) ; the head is flattened but compressed rather than depressed; the front is narrowed caudad; the lobes of the epicranium extend caudad to a considerable distance behind the meeting point of the front and vertical triangle; and there is a single large and conspicuous ocellus on each side.

Ectoedemia obrutella, E. phleophaga, and *Opostega nonstrigella* were also examined and show a similar structure except that the proleglike swellings seem to be absent. A careful study of the entire head capsule and the tentorium will be necessary before these forms can be intelligently classified.

FAMILY PRODOXIDAE

The two well-known species of this family differ markedly, having but three or four readily observed characters in common. The head is not depressed as in many Aculeata, but is about as high as wide and is considerably smaller than the prothorax. The arms of the epicranial suture unite near the vertical triangle to form a stem which separates the front from the triangle. A third character is the lack of crochets, which seems strange in caterpillars of this size. The body is round and fleshy, and wider in the middle than at the ends.

Pronuba yuccasella possesses thoracic legs and swellings representing abdominal prolegs, the latter present on segments 3, 4, 5, and 6. These proleg swellings are not found on those Gelechiidae, Coleophoridae, and Cochlidiidae which are similar enough to cause confusion.

Prodoxus quinquepunctella is without legs or leglike swellings of any kind, but the closed front is sufficient to distinguish it from such other legless larvae as have the body similarly shaped. An undescribed species from agave in Arizona was also examined and was found to be very similar.

FAMILY INCURVARIIDAE

The larvae of this family are, in some respects, nearly as generalized as any members of the order. While it is perhaps an open question as to whether the common progenitor of Aculeata possessed a front which was closed above by the union of the arms of the epicranial suture or open to the vertical triangle, the conditions in other insects and in the Micropterygidae incline one to the former view. This would place Adela and Incurvaria closer to the common ancestor of all Frenatae than the Nepticulidae.

Head as high as broad, not retractile; front reaching about two-thirds of the distance to the vertical triangle; adfrontals extending to vertical triangle. Body cylindrical, intersegmental incisions shallow or indistinct; thorax with setae in the usual position but those dorsad of kappa indistinct; abdomen with kappa and eta adjacent, close to and caudad of ventral edge of spiracle; mu and Pi group as usual; thoracic legs present; prolegs indicated only by the crochets which are in transverse bands on segments 3, 4, 5, and 6.

Adela viridella and *A. degeerella* of Europe have the short and rudimentary crochets arranged in two transverse multiserial bands (Fig. 94). Forbes considers this condition to represent the beginning of crochets in Lepidoptera, but it is much more probable that such an arrangement is merely a reduced form of the multiserial circle found in Hepialus larvae. An unidentified American species from Vermont was also examined and in it the crochets were similar.

Incurvaria koerneriella has but one uniserial row of very rudimentary crochets to represent each proleg. This is undoubtedly a degenerate condition.

FAMILY TISCHERIIDAE

This family is a highly specialized group of Aculeata and its similarity to the Gracilariidae has usually caused it to be placed with them. The presence of crochets in the total absence of thoracic legs occurs only in these two families.

Head strongly depressed, three to six times as long as high; front extending to caudal margin of head, but usually narrowed caudad to a point; ocelli six in number, uniform in size. Body distinctly moniliform as seen from above, strongly depressed; thoracic legs wanting; abdominal segments 3, 4, 5, and 6 with each proleg represented by a pair of short, transverse, uniserial rows of very small uniordinal crochets.

Tischeria malifoliella, T. complanella, and other species of this genus are common blotch-miners. The front is wider at the caudal than at the cephalic end.

Coptotriche zelleriella is similar but less common. The front is narrowed caudad to a point.

SUPERFAMILY TINEOIDEA

It is with regret that this superfamily name is used, for the word may mean almost anything. But the group which includes Tinea must receive the above title, however ambiguous the word. In the sense employed here the superfamily includes less than half of the genera included by Dyar in Tineidae. The necessity for this change is explained in the introduction to the Microlepidoptera on a preceding page.

Characters of the larvae which show the relationship of the three families included here are: first, the trisetose Kappa group on the prothorax; second, the distance by which kappa and eta are separated on the abdomen; third, the triangular front which is not open dorsad; fourth, the location of beta on the prothorax, where it is closer to the dorsomeson than alpha.

FAMILY ACROLOPHIDAE

The Acrolophidae, or Anaphorinae as they have been called, include some of the largest and most primitive of the Microlepidoptera. In addition to the structures common to the four tineoid families, Acrolophidae are differentiated by a multiserial circle of crochets (Fig. 96) and may be easily separated from Bucculatrigidae and Tineidae by the large size and the fact that kappa on the prothorax is more closely associated with theta near the spiracle than with eta in the more cephalic and more usual position (Fig. 7). *Pseudanaphora arcanella* was the only species examined.

FAMILY TINEIDAE

In this paper the Tineidae include only a few genera closely related to Tinea, such as Tineola and Scardia. They distinctly show the characters given for the superfamily Tineoidea but differ strikingly from the other three families in the following combination of characters: the setae alpha on the abdominal segments are farther apart than the setae beta, the crochets are uniordinal and are arranged in a complete uniserial circle, and the three setae forming the Kappa group on the prothorax are close together.

Scardia fiskeella (Figs. 51 to 54) was the only species examined of which the material was entirely satisfactory, altho *Tineola bisselliella* was also seen.

FAMILY BUCCULATRIGIDAE

Systematists have come to think of the genus Bucculatrix as a chronic obstacle to the satisfactory classification of the lower Micros. It has been driven ''from pillar to post'' and the end is not in sight. The situation usually consists in the positive denial of admittance to the particular family which an investigator is studying. The author erects a new family for the genus, first, because specialists on adult Microlepidoptera will not admit the validity of placing Bucculatrix in any one of the recognized families; second, because the larvae can not be closely associated with those of any other genus of which specimens have been examined. The diagnostic characters of *Bucculatrix koebelella* are as follows:

Head about as high as wide, not elongate, bearing primary setae only; front reaching about two-thirds, adfrontals all the way, to the . vertical triangle. Body cylindrical, intersegmental incisions moderate. All setae in the position usual in Microlepidoptera, except that on the abdomen, kappa and eta are widely separated and at about the same level, and that alpha is below the level of beta on segments 8 and 9. Spiracles circular. Prolegs slender and rather long, present on segments 3, 4, 5, 6, and 10, the ventral ones each bearing two transverse bands of uniordinal, well-developed crochets, the anal pair bearing a single transverse band.

FAMILY LYONETIIDAE

The small size and generalized but obscure characters of this family make the genera and species difficult to distinguish. It is often almost impossible to make out locations of setae, arrangement of ocelli, and other points ordinarily of value.

Head more or less depressed; front triangular, not extending to vertical triangle in American species; boundaries of adfrontals extending to the vertical triangle on each side; first and second ocelli usually nearly contiguous, second, third, and sixth in a vertical row cephalad of the fifth. Body cylindrical, incisions moderate. Prothorax with the Kappa group trisetose, the three setae widely separated. Abdomen with alpha much closer to dorsomeson than beta, rho located immediately above spiracle, kappa some distance caudad of spiracle, and eta between kappa and spiracle but located farther ventrad, or in some cases apparently wanting. Thoracic legs present; prolegs present on segments 3, 4, 5, and 6, each bearing a complete uniserial circle of uniordinal crochets.

The above list of characters was drawn from specimens of *Bedellia somnulentella* and verified from *Proleucoptera smilaciella*, the only other American species seen. *Leucoptera (Cemiostoma) spartifoliella* of Europe differs from them in the front, which reaches the vertical triangle, and in the crochets, which are biserial in the caudal half of the circle.

SUPERFAMILY YPONOMEUTOIDEA

Still retaining the ancestral, generalized arrangement of setae, the few forms included in the Yponomeutoidea share with the Tineoidea the distinction of being closely similar to Hepialus and the primitive type. Altho a small group, the structure is extremely varied in those characters which, in specialized forms, are constant in entire superfamilies. There are two families each of which includes larvae of at least two strikingly different forms. Some authors consider Hemerophilidae and Ethmiidae as relatives of this group but the larval structure indicates a closer union with Gelechioidea. The same is true of the genus Schreckensteinia.

Family Heliodinidae

It is clear that the "elachistid" genera now included here are more closely related to Yponomeutidae than to any other families of the order. Kappa and eta of the abdomen are distant, the Kappa group of the prothorax is trisetose, with the three setae close together, and the front extends somewhat over half the distance to the vertical triangle in some species and reaches that triangle in others; the spiracle is small and circular.

Lithariapteryx abroniaeella. Head scarcely depressed; front short. Abdomen with kappa and eta not on the same swelling, alpha directly cephalad of beta. Crochets long, uniordinal or biordinal, arranged in a complete circle.

Antispila nyssaefoliella and *Aspidiscus* sp. (?).   Head strongly depressed; front extending to vertical triangle; two pairs of ocelli large and conspicuous, the others reduced.   Thoracic and abdominal legs wanting.   Abdomen with kappa and eta distinctly separated but both on the same swelling.

FAMILY YPONOMEUTIDAE

Like the Pterophoridae this family is difficult to diagnose on account of the great variation among the different genera it includes.   At the same time there is little or no overlapping with other families.   All Yponomeutidae except Scythris and Schreckensteinia have beta below the level of alpha on the prothorax, the Kappa group trisetose on the prothorax, and kappa and eta distant on the abdomen.   No other larvae possess this combination of characters.   The Tineoidea are the closest and constitute the principal reason for introducing the alpha-beta character above.   In view of this definite combination of setal characters and the great variation in other particulars no general description is given for the family.

Schreckensteinia in the larval stage seems to be more closely related to Gelechioidea than to Plutellinae, where the more recent authorities place it.   In addition to the characters given in the following table this genus may be distinguished by the prolegs, which are long and slender and at the tip bear from four to six crochets in a circle.

The subfamilies may be separated as follows:

a. Prolegs longer than wide; crochets uniserial, either biordinal or uniordinal; Pi group on metathorax represented by a single seta.
                                                                    PLUTELLINAE

aa. Prolegs wider than long; crochets various.
  b. Body bearing numerous setae on verruca-like plates; Pi group consisting of four to eight setae on each abdominal segment.
                                                                    SCYTHRIDINAE

  bb. Body bearing primary setae only; Pi group never bearing more than two setae on thoracic or three on abdominal segments.
                                                                    YPONOMEUTINAE

Following are partial keys to the genera:

Plutellinae

a. Abdomen with kappa and eta remote, alpha and beta remote.
  b. Crochets arranged in a pseudocircle.   *Plutella*
  bb. Crochets arranged in a mesoseries.   *Cerostoma*
aa. Abdomen with kappa and eta adjacent, alpha and beta adjacent.
                                                                    Schreckensteinia

Scythridinae

a. Crochets biordinal, arranged in a complete uniserial circle. *Scythris*

Yponomeutinae

a. Pi group on metathorax consisting of two setae.
  b. Crochets arranged in a mesoseries.   *Mieza*
  bb. Crochets arranged in a multiserial circle.   *Atteva*
aa. Pi group on metathorax consisting of a single seta; crochets arranged
  in a multiserial circle.
  b. Cephalic seta of Kappa group on prothorax ventrad of the other
    two.
    c. Beta ventrad of alpha on metathorax; segment 9 with a dorsal
      shield bearing setae alpha, beta, rho, kappa, and eta.
                                                                                Zelleria
    cc. Beta caudad of alpha on metathorax.   *Swammerdamia*
  bb. Cephalic seta of Kappa group on prothorax dorsad of the other
    two; beta caudoventrad of alpha on metathorax.   *Yponomeuta*

The following species of Yponomeutidae were examined:

Plutella maculipennis	*Cerostoma rubrella*
Schreckensteinia erythriella	*Scythris magnatella*
Mieza igninix	*Atteva aurea*
Zelleria gracilariella	*Swammerdamia pyrella* (Europe)
Yponomeuta plumbella, Y. multipunctella	

FAMILY GRACILARIIDAE

The gracilarians form one of the most definitely bounded families
of the order. Whether examined in an early or a late instar, they are
distinct from the larvae of other moths. This is true in spite of the fact
that a complete change of structure takes place at the second or a later
molt. Before this molt the mandibles are horizontal and wheel-shaped,
and toothed like a buzz-saw. No such structure is known elsewhere.
The distinctive feature of the later instars is the presence of but three
pairs of ventral prolegs, located on segments 3, 4, and 5. It should be
noted that where the number of prolegs is reduced in other families, as
in some Noctuidae, Geometridae, and Nolidae, they are always present
on segment 6 and are first lost on segment 3. The prolegs of gracilarian
larvae are very short and are often not represented by swellings at all
but their location is shown by suckers or by crochets which are arranged
in various ways. Thoracic legs may be present or wanting. The setae
are so minute that their position usually can not be determined satisfac-
torily.

Three subfamilies are recognized, of one of which specimens have not been available.

Gracilariinae. Head as high as wide, shape normal; front not reaching vertical triangle. Body cylindrical, intersegmental incisions shallow. Thoracic legs present; crochets of prolegs arranged in a lateral penellipse enclosing a transverse series, all uniordinal (Fig. 103). *Gracilaria consimilella, G. violacella,* and *Ornix geminatella* were examined; and Coriscium, the only other genus, is described as being similar.

Lithocolletinae. Head depressed, strongly narrowed cephalad; front with subparallel sides, extending to vertical triangle and often widest at caudal margin of head. Body depressed, moniliform. Thoracic legs present or wanting; ventral prolegs reduced, either bearing transverse rows of crochets or modified into suckers, present on segments 3, 4, and 5.

Lithocolletis hamadryadella, L. ostensackenella, Marmara salictella, M. fulgidella, and *Cameraria* sp. (?) were studied. In Marmara both thoracic legs and crochets are present, while in Cameraria neither could be identified. The individuals of Lithocolletis varied in this regard. It is to be noted that in many cases legs are acquired at the last molt and that a persistent study of all stages will be necessary before the different genera can be distinguished with any assurance of accuracy.

FAMILY TORTRICIDAE

The family of leaf-rolling caterpillars is a remarkably uniform and generalized one. Larval structure indicates rather close relationship with both Cossidae and Gelechioidea but is not to be relied upon, for all these groups are typical Microlepidoptera in most respects and may belong to wholly different but only slightly specialized stocks. Individual fluctuating variations are rather confusing in an attempt at classification but all specimens seen will trace to the family except an occasional aberrant one. Greater difficulties are met in working with the genera. For example, about twenty percent of codling moth larvae have mu of segment 9 located on the same pinaculum with kappa and eta and will therefore not trace to Cydia. The writer has not found absolutely constant characters to distinguish the genera of this family but hopes that the synopsis given here will suggest other and possibly better means of separation. The larvae are of sufficient economic importance to warrant the expenditure of considerable time in the study of their structure.

Head not depressed; front extending from one-fourth to three-fourths of the distance to the vertical triangle; adfrontals usually touching the vertical triangle; ocelli six, variously arranged, but the sixth always rather close to the fourth and fifth. Body cylindrical or submoniliform, sometimes depressed in early but rarely in later instars. Setae of thorax and abdomen as in Figs. 39 to 42 except as noted for particular genera; rho directly cephalad of spiracle on segment 8 except in a few rare cases. Spiracles broad-elliptical in outline, somewhat larger and farther dorsad on eighth than on preceding segments. Prolegs always present on segments 3, 4, 5, 6, and 10, first four pairs each bearing a complete circle of uniordinal or biordinal crochets.

It will be noted that the subfamily Olethreutinae (Grapholithinae) is not accepted here, as no larval characters were found to justify it. The genera included under this name probably do not form a natural group. The other two subfamilies may be distinguished as follows:

a. Abdomen with kappa and eta in a horizontal line or nearly so; segment 7 with Pi group unisetose; prothorax with delta close to and ventrocephalad of beta; crochets uniordinal, sessile, poorly developed.   PHALONIINAE
aa. Abdomen with kappa and eta in a diagonal or vertical line; segment 7 with Pi group at least bisetose; prothorax with delta ventrad or ventrocaudad of beta, sometimes distant.   TORTRICINAE

Genera of Tortricinae:

a. Segment 9 with alpha close to rho and usually situated on the same pinaculum with it, not associated with beta (Fig. 42).
  b. Mu absent on segment 9 (as in Fig. 56); setae located on black and heavily chitinized pinacula; crochets uniordinal.   *Sciaphila*
 bb. Mu present on segment 9, usually associated with kappa and eta.
    c. Adfrontals extending all the way and front about two-thirds of the way to the vertical triangle.
      d. Arms of epicranial suture concave in dorsal third, meeting in an attenuate point.
        e. First abdominal segment with kappa and eta in a diagonal line; seventh, in a horizontal line (as in Fig. 45).
                                                                        Thiodia
       ee. First abdominal segment with kappa and eta in a nearly vertical line (as in Fig. 41); seventh, in a diagonal line.
          f. Mu on segment 9 located on the same pinaculum with kappa and eta (as in Fig. 46).   *Tmetocera*
                                       (In part) *Exartema*
         ff. Mu usually not located on the same pinaculum with kappa and eta (Fig. 42).   *Cydia*
    dd. Arms of epicranial suture straight in dorsal third, meeting in a regularly narrowed point.   *Eucosma*

cc. Adfrontals extending two thirds and front about one half the
distance to the vertical triangle.   *Pseudogalleria*

aa. Segment 9 with alpha as distant from rho as from beta (as in Fig.
38) and with mu, kappa, and eta present on one pinaculum (as in
Fig. 46).

  b. Pi group consisting of only two setae on abdominal segment 7 and
often only one on segment 8.   *Alceris*

  bb. Pi group trisetose on abdominal segment 7 and bisetose on segment 8.

    c. Middle seta of trisetose Kappa group on prothorax dorsad of the
other two.   *Epagoge*

    cc. Middle seta of Kappa group on prothorax ventrad of or in line
with the other two.

      d. Middle seta of Kappa group on prothorax at least three times
as far from caudal as from cephalic seta.

        e. Mesothorax and metathorax with Pi group bisetose (as in
Fig. 50).   *Archips* (a)

        ee. Mesothorax and metathorax with Pi group unisetose
(Fig. 40)

          f. Second ocellus much farther from first than from third.
(Fig. 80).   *Platynota*
                                              Archips (b)

        ff. Second ocellus as close to first as to third (Fig. 71).
Ancylis
Olethreutes
Tortrix
Episimus
Cenopis

      dd. Middle seta of Kappa group on prothorax not more than
twice as far from caudal as from cephalic seta.

        e. Fourth ocellus much closer to third than to sixth and caudad
of line joining third and sixth.   *Ecdytolophia*

        ee. Fourth ocellus about half way between third and sixth and
in line with them. (Fig. 70).   *Enarmonia*

Lord Walsingham in a recent volume of the Biologia Centrali-
Americana changes to some extent the generic location of species in the
Tortricidae. Three of his transfers are adopted here, the former genus
names being included in parenthesis; but in several other instances, the
change does not seem to be supported by the evidence of larval structure.
The following were the species examined:

PHALONIINAE.

Phalonia hilarana (Europe)

TORTRICINAE

Sciaphila wahlbomiana (Europe)
Thiodia arctostaphylana
Exartema malana, E. exoletum
Tmetocera ocellana
Cydia pomonella, C. (Melissopus) latiferreanus, C. saltitans
Eucosma pulsatillana, E. scudderiana, E. (Proteopteryx) willingana Kearf.
Pseudogalleria inimicella
Alceris minuta, A. hastiana, A. foliana, A. brittania Kearf.
Epagoge sulphureana, E. caryae
Archips (a) *cerasivorana, A. fervidana, A. parallela*
Archips (b) *argyrospila, A. negundana, A. rosaceana*
Platynota labiosana
Olethreutes niveiguttana, O. (Eudemis) vacciniana
Ancylis comptana, A. divisana, A. nubeculana
Tortrix fumiferana, T. quercifoliana, T. citrana
Episimus argutanus
Cenopis directana Walk., *C. pettitana* Robsn.
Ecdytolophia insiticiana
Enarmonia caryana, E. nebritana, E. prunivora

FAMILY THYRIDIDAE.

Head smaller than prothorax, bearing primary setae only; ocelli six, arranged in a regular semicircle; labrum moderately emarginate; front reaching more than half way to vertical triangle. Body regularly cylindrical; intersegmental incisions shallow. Prothorax with a shield bearing rho near epsilon below alpha and gamma; Kappa group trisetose. Mesothorax and metathorax with Pi group bisetose. First eight abdominal segments with alpha farther laterad than beta, epsilon absent or very minute, kappa and eta borne on the same pinaculum, Pi group consisting of two setae on segment 1, three setae on segments 2 to 6, two setae on 7, one seta on 8; abdominal segment 9 with alpha closer to dorsomeson than beta (Fig. 55). Prolegs with biordinal crochets in a complete circle; anal prolegs with transverse series of crochets. Spiracles elliptical, small.

The above characterization was made from *Thyris fenestrella* of Europe and *Dysodia oculatana* of America, the chaetotaxy of the two being constant. The bisetose Pi group of the last two thoracic segments and the arrangement of the setae on segment 9 of the abdomen will distinguish this family from all others. The affinities are clearly with the true Microlepidoptera, not with the Zygaenoidea or Bombycoidea.

Thyris differs from Dysodia in the shape of the front, which in the former is nearly as broad as high, with adfrontals bounded by straight lines, while in Dysodia it is long and narrow with nearly parallel sides and the adfrontals are widened above.

Three other genera with unknown larvae are recorded from North America, in addition to Thyridopyralis. The latter does not belong in this family. As the name indicates, the imaginal characters conflict, but those of the larva clearly place *T. gallaerandalis,* the only species, in Pyralididae, subfamily Phycitinae. The pyralid structures are the bisetose Kappa group of the prothorax, the unisetose Pi group of the other thoracic segments, and the position of alpha on segment 9 where it is farther laterad than beta.

FAMILY AEGERIIDAE.

Sesiidae, the name used in Dyar's List for this family, is the one by which it is best known, but as it has been discarded in all the more recent systematic work, there seems to be no reason for continuing the error. It appears to be clearly established that Sesia belongs in Sphingidae and that Aegeria is the oldest genus in the family.

The larvae are well known borers and at least two of them are serious and very common enemies of the peach. All are so uniform that their separation is difficult. A key to the known species has been published by Dyar (Beutenmüller, 1900). The one given below is based on practically the same species but employs different characters, and it is hoped that later workers will add to the number of good generic distinctions as well as to the number of known larvae. The following characters are common to all the species:

Head smaller than prothorax, with strong mandibles; front and ocelli various; labrum shallowly concave at tip. Body cylindrical, incisions rather deep. Prothorax with beta farther mesad than alpha and with Kappa group trisetose, mesothorax and metathorax as in Tortricidae (Fig. 40). Abdomen with kappa and eta adjacent and other setae as usual except that they are disarranged on segment 8 by the change in the position of the spiracle; segment 9 with all setae in a single transverse row (Fig. 57). Spiracles broad and elliptical, much larger and higher on eighth than on other abdominal segments. Prolegs always bearing two transverse bands of uniordinal crochets (Fig. 99).

Genera of Aegeriidae:

a. The three caudodorsal ocelli forming a triangle with an acute angle
   at the second ocellus (Fig. 77) ; seta kappa on metathorax at least
   two and one-half times as far from eta as from theta.*
b. Vertical triangle longer than wide, touching adfrontals.
                                                     Vespamima
bb. Vertical triangle broadly rounded, wider than long, usually not
   touching adfrontals.
   c. Crochets not more than nine in number, large and thick; setae
     large and distinct.   *Parharmonia*
   cc. Crochets usually over ten in number, when fewer they are small
     and slender; setae reduced.
     d. Adfrontals uniform in width, sides straight or convex.
                                                *Sanninoidea**
     dd. Adfrontals strongly narrowed near frontal seta, margins sin-
       uate, concave in part of their course.   *Aegeria*
aa. The three caudodorsal ocelli forming a triangle always with an
   obtuse angle at the second ocellus (Fig. 75) ; seta kappa of metathorax never more than twice as far from eta as from theta.
  b. Spiracles of eighth abdominal segment located subdorsally, at least
   six times as far apart as each is wide; annulets distinct.
   c. Crochets fifteen to eighteen in a row; adfrontal margins touch-
     ing vertical triangle.   *Podosesia*
   cc. Crochets less than fifteen or more than eighteen in number;
     adfrontals usually not touching vertical triangle.   *Memythrus*
  bb. Spiracles of segment 8 located on the dorsum, less than four times
   as far apart as each is wide; annulets indistinct; setae very small.
                                                  Melittia

The following species were studied in arranging the above table:

    Vespamima sequoiae
    Parharmonia pini
    Sanninoidea exitiosa, S. opalescens
    Aegeria (Synanthedon) pictipes, A. rutilans, A. castaneae
    Podosesia syringae
    Memythrus polistiformis, M. robinae, M. tricinctus, M. brillians
    Melittia satyriniformis

In addition, Dyar in the paper referred to above describes the
following:

---

*Each species of Sanninoidea differs somewhat from one or the other of the
two characters included in "a"; both characters must therefore be tried.

Bembecia marginata. Crochets very small, ten to fifteen in a row; spiracles slightly chitinized; setae strongly developed; segments triannulate; adfrontals not reaching vertical triangle.

Alcathoe caudata. Similar to Bembecia except that the crochets are larger and are heavily chitinized.

Family Cossidae.

The Carpenter moths received their popular name from the larval habit of boring in trees. This form of life has modified the structure, especially of the head, and has caused the development of rather heavily chitinized pinacula for relatively reduced setae. Many of the species attain considerable size and their larvae are some of our largest caterpillars.

Head broad, usually longer, if not higher, than wide, smaller than prothorax to which it is closely united; front varying from one third to one half height of head; dorsal four ocelli forming nearly a semicircle distant from the fourth and fifth; labrum truncate at tip, with a scarcely perceptible emargination; mandibles very large. (Fig. 72.) Body widest at prothorax, narrowest at beginning of abdomen, bearing primary setae only. Prothorax with rho directly caudad of epsilon, Kappa group trisetose. Mesothorax and metathorax as in Tortricidae (Fig. 40). Abdomen with kappa and eta adjacent; epsilon usually present cephalad of spiracle, sometimes large; beta above level of alpha on segment 9. Prolegs present on segment 3, 4, 5, 6, and 10; crochets various.

Genera of Cossidae:

a. Crochets uniordinal, arranged in two transverse bands; prothorax bearing a large, dorsal, semicircular, rugose plate on its caudal half; spiracles of segment 8 two or three times as large as those of segments 1 to 7 and located much nearer dorsomeson.   *Cossula*
aa. Crochets biordinal or triordinal, arranged in a complete circle.
  b. Prothoracic shield with the caudal margin smooth and not elevated; spiracle of segment 8 in line with those of segments 1 to 7, below rho.
    c. Setae alpha of middle abdominal segments only two-thirds as far apart on dorsum as setae beta.   *Prionoxystus*
    cc. Setae alpha of middle abdominal segments more than three-fourths as far apart as setae beta (in American species).
                                                 Cossus
  bb. Prothoracic shield with the dorsal half of the caudal margin conspicuous and strongly rugose; spiracle of segment 8 higher than those of segments 1 to 7, caudad of rho.   *Zeuzera*

Cossula magnifica is so different from other cossid larvae that at first it seems to deserve the rank of a separate subfamily. Certain European larvae form a series connecting this type with the others, hence such a division could not be defended. For example, in *Phragmatoecia castaneae* Hübner, the crochets are uniordinal but arranged in a complete circle and the last pair of spiracles are enlarged and moved dorsad as in *Cossula; Dyspessa ulula* Borkh. has rudimentary crochets in indefinite transverse rows but all the spiracles are in line.

Prionoxystus robiniae is our most common species. The larva, which bores in locust and other trees, often reaches a length of three inches. *P. macmurtrei*, the only other species, is smaller and bores in a number of different trees. The crochets of the latter species are circular in arrangement while those of the former are in a very narrow ellipse.

Cossus centerensis has a larval structure nearly identical with that of Prionoxystus. The two are hard to distinguish and the character given in the table does not hold for European species of Cossus. There is a Rocky Mountain species, the larva of which I have not seen.

Zeuzera pyrina has a world-wide distribution. Like *Cossula magnifica,* it is distinct from the other forms and is the only species of the genus found in North America.

Larvae of the western genus Hypopta and the subtropical Inguromorpha have not been seen.

Family Psychidae

The Bagworm moths are a peculiar group which Dyar at one time considered as deserving the erection of a separate suborder. He seems later to have abandoned this view, which was based on the fact that alpha and beta are located on the same annulet of the abdominal segments instead of on successive ones. The homology seems clear enough altho the position of the setae is, it is true, different from that found in other larvae. This combined with the absolutely unique horizontal prothoracic spiracle shows that the family is an ancient one. The different genera are remarkably uniform.

Head overarched by the prothorax above but large and not truly retractile; front and adfrontals various; labrum notched to about half its depth; ocelli normal. Body with primary setae only, these very minute in later stages. Prothorax with all setae normal, Kappa group trisetose, epsilon and rho distant from each other; mesothorax and metathorax normal except that the Pi group is bisetose. Abdomen with alpha, beta, and rho in almost a straight line above the spiracle, but alpha and beta close together on segment 9; kappa and eta adjacent; mu present; Pi group normal. Prolegs present as usual on segments 3,

4, 5, 6, and 10, the crochets arranged in the same uniordinal, lateral penellipse on the anal as on the ventral pairs (Fig. 85). Spiracles elliptical, the prothoracic pair much larger than those of the abdomen and placed horizontally (Fig. 69).

While the body setae offer some characters of taxonomic importance in separating the genera, I hesitate to use them on account of their great reduction. In many cases it is impossible to find them without a prolonged search. This is not true, however, of the head setae, whose location is distinct. The fact that their position varies with the different genera is fortunate, for the coloration and general shape of the body are too constant to aid in identification.

In the following synopsis the division into Solenobiinae and Psychinae is retained and some new facts are added to the characters Forbes used in their separation. With one exception his larvae were of different species from the ones mentioned below.

Genera of Psychidae:

a. Second adfrontal seta much farther dorsad than frontal seta, first
    adfrontal seta above level of top of front (Fig. 83); thoracic legs
    with last two segments very slender; alpha of abdomen above level
    of beta. (Solenobiinae.)   *Solenobia*

aa. Second adfrontal seta very close to frontal seta, first adfrontal seta
    below level of top of front (Figs. 76, 79, 82); thoracic legs with
    last two segments stout; alpha of abdomen below level of beta.
    (Psychinae.)

  b. Margins of adfrontals meeting dorsad at an acute angle, adfrontals
      scarcely widened above first adfrontal seta (Fig. 76); larvae
      small, pale, not exceeding two centimeters in length.
                                                 Eurycittarus

  bb. Margins of adfrontals meeting dorsad at a very obtuse angle or
      in a horizontal line; larvae three to five centimeters in length in
      last stage, usually dark in color.

    c. Frontal seta located below line connecting second adfrontal seta
       with frontal puncture (Fig. 78).   *Thyridopteryx*
    cc. Frontal seta located above line connecting second adfrontal seta
       with frontal puncture (Fig. 82).   *Oiketicus*

The following species were studied: *Solenobia walshella, Eurycittarus confederata, Thyridopteryx ephemeraeformis,* and *Oiketicus abbotii.* All are approximately unicolorous except for a tendency to longitudinal light and dark stripes on the thorax, especially on the dorsal half. Two other species, *Platoeceticus gloveri* of Florida and *Chalia rileyi* of the ''Atlantic States'' are found east of the Rockies but they are rather rare and their larvae, so far as I know, have not been recognized.

FAMILY ELACHISTIDAE

The Tineidae and Elachistidae have long been dumping grounds for all manner of Microlepidoptera. It is within the last five or six years (1909) that Busck has pointed out the necessity of dividing and redividing these "families". The Elachistidae appear to contain six well defined groups, five in addition to those related to Elachista. These are now known as Cycnidioidea, Coleophoridae, Cosmopterygidae, Heliodinidae, and Scythridinae of Yponomeutidae. Larvae of the true Elachistidae and of the superfamily Cycnidioidea have not been examined. Scythridinae and Heliodinidae are discussed in their proper place in the Yponomeutoidea. Cosmopterygidae will be found under Gelechioidea while Coleophoridae apparently do not belong in any of the superfamilies listed in this paper.

FAMILY COLEOPHORIDAE

Head scarcely depressed; front extending about two-thirds, adfrontals all the way to the vertical triangle; ocelli all close together, seta vii closest to second ocellus, fourth ocellus usually as close to sixth as to fifth. Body cylindrical, setae almost indistinguishable, apparently in the normal microlepidopterous arrangement. Thoracic legs about as far apart as the width of the coxae; ventral prolegs each bearing two transverse uniserial bands of uniordinal crochets, usually so close to ventromeson that the bands of the right and left sides are nearly continuous with each other; anal prolegs each with a single transverse row close to ventromeson. Crochets reduced in number in some species, either rudimentary and reduced from two to six for each proleg as in *Coleophora fletcherella*, or entirely wanting as in *C. limospenella*. Spiracles small, circular, those of the eighth abdominal segment twice as large and slightly farther dorsad than those of other segments.

The following species of Coleophora were seen, all of them having transverse rows of crochets except as noted above: *tiliaefoliella, atriplicivora, fletcherella, gallipenella, ochripenella, limospenella,* and several others unidentified.

SUPERFAMILY GELECHIOIDEA

This group includes the most highly specialized of the tineoid series of Microlepidoptera. Some of the families are difficult to separate in any stage, especially as Gelechia seems to be rather a generalized genus from which several others diverged. The characters are such that the interrelations of the families can not be worked out from them altho there are a sufficient number of differences to separate them more or less completely from each other.

FAMILY ETHMIIDAE

This family was named and described in 1909 by Busck to accommodate the genus Ethmia, hitherto included in Oecophoridae. The new family was based wholly on characters of the adult, hence it is a striking fact that the larvae of Ethmia are distinctly different from those of any of the other genera usually associated with it. Unfortunately the larvae of but two species, *E. zelleriella* and *E. longimaculella,* were available, but their characters are important enough to make the following record of them desirable.

Head smaller than prothorax, bearing primary setae only; front with dorsal half of lateral margins straight; adfrontals not reaching vertical triangle; labrum moderately emarginate at tip; ocelli six, the fourth, fifth, and sixth forming a triangle with an acute angle at the fourth, the fourth farther from the fifth than from the sixth. Prothorax with alpha slightly closer to dorsomeson than beta, other setae in usual positions; mesothorax and metathorax normal. Abdomen with alpha above level of beta, rho dorsad of spiracle on segments 1 to 7, cephalad on segment 8, kappa and eta adjacent, mu present, Pi group various, sigma present. Prolegs short, with an extended *mesoseries* of biordinal crochets. Spiracles elliptical, slightly larger on segment 8 but no higher on body.

In *Ethmia zelleriella* the Pi group of the abdominal segments is trisetose as usual, while in *E. longimaculella* the number is increased to eight or ten setae. In neither species, however, is there any increase of setae on the thorax.

FAMILY STENOMIDAE

Recent study has shown that moths belonging to the genera Stenoma, Brachiloma, and Ide do not belong to the Australian family Xylorictidae where they were formerly placed, but constitute a separate group. According to Busck the three genera should be united under the name Stenoma.

Head rather broad and depressed, the mouth parts directed cephalad; front extending less than half way to vertex, and adfrontals little farther; labrum distinctly but not deeply emarginate; ocelli six; primary setae only. Body depressed, the spiracles somewhat below the middle of the lateral aspect. Prothorax with rho near epsilon below gamma, and the Kappa group trisetose; other two thoracic segments with Pi group unisetose. Abdomen with kappa and eta adjacent, beta farther laterad than alpha except on segment 8 where they are at about the same level, and segment 9 where it is farther mesad; kappa, eta, and mu on segment 9 located on the same pinaculum. Thoracic legs adjacent, prolegs short, each bearing a complete circle of biordinal crochets; anal prolegs bearing a single series of crochets on the cephalic margin.

Stenoma humilis has a small head, uniform in color and less than one-third the diameter of the body, while in *S. schlaegeri* and *S. brillians* Busck the head is about two-thirds the width of the body and is transversely striped, the stripe continuous in the former but broken and dotted in the latter.

Gonioterma albanum of Europe differs from the American species in that the Kappa group on segments 7 and 8 is cephalo-ventrad of rho while in Stenoma it is directly ventrad.

Family Hemerophilidae

Several important differences may be noted, distinguishing the larvae of this family from those of the Yponomeutidae, in which they have long been included. The most important is the close association of kappa and eta on the abdomen and the relative position of alpha and beta on the prothorax.

Head longer than wide; front much longer than wide, acute at caudal end, extending more than half way to vertical triangle; adfrontals narrow; ocelli all close together. Prothorax with alpha farther laterad than beta, rho distant from epsilon, Kappa group trisetose, and Pi group unisetose as usual; metathorax similar. Abdomen with spiracles round or broadly elliptical, beta farther laterad than alpha on all segments except 9, where alpha is usually much farther from dorsomeson; kappa and eta adjacent. Prolegs long and slender, with either a complete circle or mesoseries of uniordinal crochets, often poorly developed.

Four of the genera belonging to this family have been examined in the larval stage.

Choreutis leucobasis. Crochets rudimentary, arranged in a complete circle; Pi group on segments 2, 7, and 8 trisetose; all setae poorly developed; alpha and beta at about the same level on abdominal segments.

Allonyma (Hemerophila) vicarilis. Crochets strongly chitinized; setae well developed and borne on distinct pinacula; otherwise similar to Choreutis.

Brenthia pavonacella. Crochets in a complete circle; beta almost directly ventrad of alpha on abdominal segments 1 to 8, caudad of alpha on segment 9.

Trichostibas parvula Edwards.	Crochets in a mesoseries; beta caudad of alpha on abdominal segments 1 to 8, dorsocaudad of alpha on segment 9; Pi group unisetose on segments 2, 7, and 8.

Family Gelechiidae

The enumeration of Gelechiidae in Dyar's List is considered as very nearly correct and will be followed more closely than is possible with most other families of Microlepidoptera. Larvae of this family will be most often confused with Pyralididae and Tortricidae on account of similarity in size and habit. The distinctly trisetose Kappa group of the prothorax will differentiate from the former and the distance of setae beta on segment 9 will distinguish from the latter. It seems unnecessary to enumerate such characters as the location of all the setae, for the larvae are typical Micros, any important differences from the usual plan (Figs. 39-42) being noted in the tables. It might be mentioned in addition that the crochets are biordinal except in a few degenerate cases, that the front and adfrontals are very acute above, the adfrontals often reaching the vertical triangle, that the spiracles are circular in outline, those of segment 8 usually being larger and higher on the body, and that the ocelli are almost never arranged as described for Oecophoridae (cf. Figs. 80 and 81).

The following synopsis of the genera is incomplete, owing partially to lack of material, but is an arrangement which can be developed further as the larvae of more species become known.

a. Crochets wanting or reduced and rudimentary; no proleg swellings
     present; thoracic legs small.
  b. Body swollen and strongly tapering at ends.	*Metzneria*
  bb. Body nearly cylindrical, scarcely tapering.	*Sitotroga*
aa. Crochets present and well developed.
  b. Crochets of ventral prolegs in a complete circ e, usually biordinal;
       those of anal prolegs in a continuous transverse series.
    c. Prolegs long and slender; crochets few; setae rudimentary; head
         retractile.	*Nealyda*
    cc. Prolegs short and stout, crochets usually numerous.
      d. Setae rho of segment 8 cephalad, rarely cephalodorsad of spiracle; body always striped; setae large.
        e. Abdominal segment 7 with setae beta closer together on
             dorsum than setae alpha; segment 8 with setae beta farther apart than setae alpha.	*Arogalea*
        ee. Segments 7 and 8 both with setae beta farther apart than
             setae alpha.

f. Triangle formed by the three cephaloventral ocelli having a right or obtuse angle at the fourth ocellus, the fifth as close to the fourth as to the sixth; coloration consisting wholly of transverse stripes.   *Telphusa*

ff. Triangle formed by the three cephaloventral ocelli always having an acute angle at the fourth ocellus, the fifth about equidistant from the fourth and sixth; coloration almost always including longitudinal stripes. *Gelechia*
        Recurvaria

dd. Seta rho of segment 8 dorsad, rarely cephalodorsad, of spiracle; body caudad of prothorax entirely pale; setae minute.

e. Head and prothorax usually strongly chitinized and black.
        Phthorimaea

ee. Head and prothorax slightly chitinized and pale.
        Gnorimoschema

bb. Crochets of ventral prolegs in a pair of transverse bands, usually biordinal, those of anal prolegs in two groups, prolegs short; spiracle of abdominal segment 8 very large. *Ypsolophus*
        Anarsia
        Trichotaphe
        Anacampsis

The species of Gelechia vary greatly.

The difference between Gnorimoschema and Phthorimaea, as given, is certainly not one of generic value but may serve to separate the two species studied. It is unlikely that the collector east of the Mississippi will find larvae belonging to other species. According to Busck the two genera should be united.

The following species were studied, in most cases two to six individuals being seen. The variation is a serious problem only in the genus Gelechia.

Metzneria lapella
Sitotroga cerealella
Nealyda bifidella
Arogalea (Paralechia) cristifasciella
Telphusa fuscopunctella
Recurvaria sp. (?)
Phthorimaea operculella
Gnorimoschema gallaesolidaginis
Trichotaphe serrativatella, T. alacella
Anarsia lineatella
Ypsolophus ligulellus
Anacampsis populella, A. lagunculariella, A. innocuella

Gelechia trialbamaculella, G. cercerisella, G. hibiscella, G. unctulella, G. maculimarginella, G. pseudacaciella, and *G. serotinella* of North America, and *G. atriplicella, G. acuminatella, G. rhombella,* and *G. mulinella* of Europe.

Family Oecophoridae

This is one of the families formerly included in Gelechiidae and the larvae are so similar to the latter that no satisfactory character has been found to distinguish the two groups. They seem to divide along the same lines on the basis of the position of rho on segment 8 of the abdomen. In all the species seen the adfrontals extend to the vertical triangle, the prolegs are short and stout and bear a complete circle of biordinal crochets and the prothoracic shield is lightly chitinized. The fourth ocellus is always much closer to the third than to the sixth, and the second is always farther from the first than from the third. Otherwise the characters are the same as in Gelechiidae.

Depressaria is the best known genus in the family. As a rule the setae are located on heavily chitinized pinacula, often elevated and chalaza-like; kappa and eta of the abdomen are borne on a small pinaculum directly ventrad of rho, eta being located cephalodorsad of kappa on the first two or three abdominal segments; rho on segment 8 is always a little above the level of the top of the spiracle, tho located farther cephalad on the segment. *Depressaria heracliana* and *D. cinereocostella* of America and *D. depressella* of Europe were seen.

Agonopteryx Hübner has recently been separated from *Depressaria* altho the difference between the two is very slight in any stage. This genus agrees with all the characters given in the preceding paragraph except that eta is cephaloventrad of kappa on the first two or three abdominal segments. The species examined were *A. umbraticostella, A. lythrella,* and *A. posticella,* all of North America.

Machimia tentoriferella is a larva with indistinct and slightly chitinized setae and with obscure or absent pinacula; rho on segment 8 is cephalad of the spiracle and at the same level; kappa and eta are below the spiracle and located farther caudad than rho.

Psilocorsis quercicella and *P. obsoletella,* formerly included in *Cryptolechia,* are closely related to the other two genera mentioned and their characters indicate an intermediate position. The pinacula are distinct, rho on segment 8 is directly cephalad of the spiracle and kappa and eta are on a pinaculum ventrad of rho.

Oecophora similella, Dasystoma salicella, and *Chimabache fagella,* of Europe, are similar in all important particulars to the American forms.

Family Blastobasidae

The larvae of this family are very similar to the last two discussed but a few differences remain. Rho, on abdominal segment 8, is caudo-dorsad of the spiracle, while kappa is cephaloventrad, an arrangement found in no other larvae. The prolegs are short and bear a complete series of uniordinal crochets, which are, however, sometimes irregular. Only primary setae are present on the body. Ocelli indefinite in specimens examined.

The species seen were: *Valentinia glandulella* Riley and *Holcocera gigantella* Ch. of North America and *Endrosis lacteella* of Europe.

Family Cosmopterygidae

Head more or less depressed, very much so in *Cosmopteryx*, small, retractile within prothorax; adfrontals not quite reaching vertical triangle; ocelli all close together, seta vii closest to second ocellus, fourth ocellus usually as close to sixth as to fifth. Setae of body small; abdomen with kappa and eta adjacent; setae beta of segment 9 much farther apart than each is from alpha of that side, beta, alpha, and rho in a transverse line. Thoracic legs with coxae twice as far apart as wide; prolegs far apart, each bearing a complete circle of uniordinal *(Stilbosis)* or biordinal crochets.

The following species were examined:

Cosmopteryx gemmiferella, C. clandestinella,
Limnoecia phragmitiella,
Homaledra sobalella, H. heptathalama, and
Stilbosis tesquella, of America, and
Cosmopteryx scribalella,
Heydenia fulvigutella, and
Laverna phragmitella of Europe.

SUPERFAMILY PYRALIDOIDEA

Scarcely half a dozen characters are common to all the larvae within this superfamily. The deciding factors are the presence of a bisetose Kappa group on the prothorax and the close association of kappa and eta on the abdomen. Some of the Pterophoridae have these points obscured by secondary and tufted setae, and such incidental structures as the circular spiracles and the long slender prolegs must be used in determination. (Figs. 47, 48, 61.)

Unless care is taken in observing the number of setae on the prolegs, *Lacosoma* will trace to this superfamily. It is distinguished from Pyralidoidea by the Pi group which consists of from four to eight setae.

Family Pyralididae

The superfamily character of a bisetose Kappa group on the prothorax, combined with the presence of short prolegs bearing either a pair of transverse bands or a more or less complete circle of biordinal crochets, limits the family. In some specimens of *Galleria mellonella* the crochets seem to be uniordinal but no individuals have been seen in which that was true of all the prolegs.

The family includes four main divisions typified by the following four subfamilies: Chrysauginae, Galleriinae, Phycitinae, and Pyraustinae. The species of the first two are few in number while each of the others is very large in addition to being associated with several smaller subfamilies. The structural basis of these divisions is shown by the following synopsis:

a. Crochets uniordinal, arranged in two transverse bands; front extending nearly and adfrontals entirely to vertical triangle.
                                                    Chrysauginae
aa. Crochets arranged in a pseudocircle or penellipse, very rarely uniordinal.
  b. Pi group on mesothorax and metathorax bisetose; crochets sometimes uniordinal (Fig. 50).   Galleriinae
  bb. Pi group on mesothorax and metathorax unisetose; crochets always biordinal or triordinal.
    c. Kappa and mu present on segment 9, usually associated with eta on the same pinaculum (Fig. 46); crochets arranged in a complete circle.   Epipaschiinae
                                                    Pyralidinae
                                                    Phycitinae
    cc. Kappa and mu absent or extremely minute on segment 9, eta well developed, not associated with other setae (Fig. 49).
      d. Crochets arranged in a penellipse.
        e. Crochets biordinal.   (In part) Crambinae
        ee. Crochets triordinal (Fig. 98).   Pyraustinae
      dd. Crochets arranged in a complete circle.
        e. Crochets triordinal.   (In part) Crambinae
        ee. Crochets biordinal.   (See also subfamily descriptions.)
                                                    Nymphulinae
                                                    Scopariinae

Chrysauginae. This subfamily must have been separated from other pyralids at a rather remote period in their history, for intermediate stages are lost and the differences, especially in the crochets, are striking. The chaetotaxy is as in the other subfamilies but it may be noted that the Pi group on the mesothorax and metathorax is unisetose, that alpha on segment 9 is about as far from rho as from beta, and that kappa, eta, and mu are present and subequal in size, but not closely associated with each other. The species examined was *Clydonopteron (Salobrana) tecomae*.

Galleriinae. Aside from their peculiar habits as pests of beehives, these larvae are easy to recognize by distinctive structures as well. The Pi group on the last two thoracic segments is bisetose; the two setae of the Kappa group on the prothorax as well as the abdomen are nearly in a horizontal line instead of a vertical one as usual; the crochets are either biordinal or uniordinal, never triordinal, and are arranged in a complete circle; alpha, beta, and rho on segment 9 form an equilateral triangle, rho being directly ventrad of beta.

Two species were examined. In *Galleria mellonella* (=*cereana*) the body is thickened in the middle and tapering towards both ends and the coxae of the metathoracic legs are twice as far apart as wide. In *Achroia grisella* the body is cylindrical and the thoracic legs are close together.

Epipaschiinae. This small group is a closely circumscribed one with characters which associate it with Phycitinae. A few of the latter show nearly all the peculiarities of this subfamily, so Epipaschiinae are introduced into the table for the separation of the genera of Phycitinae instead of being separated from them in the synopsis of the subfamilies. The crochets are triordinal, the longest about four times the length of the shortest. Other characters are given in the synopsis of Phycitinae.

The following species were examined: *Epipaschia superatalis, E. zelleri, Jocara perseella* B. & McD., *Tetralopha militella, T. floridella,* and *T. robustella.*

Pyralidinae. While the structure of the three species of Pyralidinae* examined is quite constant, it is almost impossible to find a character which will distinguish them from Phycitinae as a whole. They will be found in the table of genera of the latter group. In *Pyralis farinalis* the crochets are biordinal, the shorter ones about one-fourth the length of the others (Fig. 101), but those of *Omphalocera dentosa* and *O. cariosa* are as in the two related subfamilies. In all three species beta is clearly in the caudad row of the setae on the prothoracic shield and is scarcely farther cephalad than delta; the third and fourth ocelli are close together and the fourth out of line; the front extends about half way to vertical triangle and the adfrontals about two-thirds; and the head is about as broad as long. In color *Pyralis* is pale while the species of *Omphalocera* are dark with white pinacula.

---

*The larva of *Hypsopygia costalis,* examined since writing the above, agrees with Pyralis with respect to the prolegs, and will trace near to this genus in the key.

Phycitinae. This group and Pyraustinae are the two large sub-families of Pyralididae and many of the larvae of both of them are of economic importance. They represent two diverging lines of evolution, the one characterized by a complete circle of crochets on the prolegs and the presence of kappa and mu on segment 9, the other losing the lateral crochets of the prolegs as well as kappa and mu on segment 9. Associated with Phycitinae in the former division are the two subfamilies just discussed, and all three are included together in a single synopsis of the genera, those belonging to Pyralidinae being marked with an asterisk (*).

Genera of Phycitinae, Pyralinae, and Epipaschiinae:

a. Prothorax with delta twice as far caudad of beta as beta is of alpha, alpha and beta usually closely associated (Fig. 47).
   b. Head longer than broad; body unicolorous, dark.	*Thyridopyralis*
   bb. Head broader than long.
      c. Boundaries of adfrontals meeting epicranial suture at a point nearly twice as far from vertical triangle as from front; coloration in longitudinal stripes.	*Meroptera*
      cc. Boundaries of adfrontals meeting epicranial suture at a point half way between vertical triangle and front.
         d. Kappa nearly directly caudad of eta on first abdominal segment; fourth ocellus about as close to sixth as to third.	*Euzophera*
         dd. Kappa directly dorsad of eta on first abdominal segment; fourth ocellus farther from sixth than from third.
            e. Pinacula of all setae heavily chitinized; body widened at middle.	*Melitara*
            ee. Pinacula of all setae slightly chitinized; body cylindrical.	*Salebria*
aa. Prothorax with delta much less than twice as far caudad of beta as beta is of alpha, beta and delta often closely associated (Fig. 43).
   b. Beta of prothorax nearly directly dorsad of delta; head and body pale (Fig. 43).	*Psorosina*
   bb. Beta of prothorax located much farther cephalad than delta.
      c. Boundaries of adfrontals reaching vertical triangle.
         d. Vertical triangle nearly as large as front; prothoracic shield black.	*Elasmopalpus*
         dd. Vertical triangle normal, small; prothoracic shield pale; pinacula slightly chitinized.	*Hulstea*
      cc. Boundaries of adfrontals not reaching vertical triangle.
         d. Kappa of first abdominal segment directly dorsad of eta; boundaries of adfrontals meeting in an acute point.

e. Three ventral ocelli not forming an equilateral triangle,
angle at sixth ocellus right or obtuse (Fig. 71).
> f. Front extending about two-thirds of the distance to ver-
tical triangle; adfrontals meeting epicranial suture about
half way between front and vertical triangle.   *Plodia*
> ff. Front extending about half way to vertical triangle.
>> g. Boundaries of adfrontals meeting epicranial suture about
half way between front and vertical triangle; crochets
biordinal, the longer four times the length of the
shorter (Fig. 101).   *Pyralis**
>> gg. Boundaries of adfrontals meeting epicranial suture
at a point about twice as far from the vertical triangle
as from front; crochets triordinal.   *Ephestia*
Vitula
ee. Three ventral ocelli forming an equilateral triangle, acute
angle at each ocellus (Fig. 70); front reaching about half
way to vertical triangle.
> f. Head rugose; body dark.   *Acrobasis*
> ff. Head smooth.   *Mineola* (a)
dd. Kappa of first abdominal segment directly caudad of eta or
nearly so; front extending about half way to vertical
triangle.
> e. Second ocellus not closer to third than to first; body not
striped.
>> f. Lateral margins of adfrontals convex dorsad, meeting in
an obtuse angle; body dark, not spotted.   *Tacoma*
>> ff. Lateral margins of adfrontals nearly straight, meeting in
an acute angle.
>>> g. Body and pinacula pale.   *Canarsia*
Mineola (b)
>>> gg. Body black with white pinacula.   *Omphalocera**
> ee. Second ocellus much closer to third than to first; first ocel-
lus larger than others; lateral margins of front very convex; body striped, usually longitudinally. (See subfamily.)   Epipaschiinae

The following species of Phycitinae were examined:
Thyridopyralis gallaerandalis (heretofore included in Thyrididae)
Meroptera pravella
Euzophera ostricolorella   *Melitara prodenialis*
Salebria contatella   *Psorosina (Canarsia) hammondi*
Elasmopalpus lignosellus   *Hulstea undulatella*
Plodia interpunctella   *Ephestia kuehniella, E. cautella*

Vitula edmandsii

Mineola indiginella (a)

   M. amplexella (b)

Tacoma nyssaecolella

Acrobasis betulella

   A. comptoniella

   A. stigmella Dyar

Canarsia ulmiarrosorella

Crambinae. The larvae of many species of Crambus are of economic importance and should be familiar to entomologists. They can not readily be differentiated from each other, but can be distinguished from other groups. Any larva with a complete circle of triordinal crochets, with but two setae in front of the prothoracic spiracle, with a single seta on segment 9 caudad of the spiracle on segment 8 and with but one seta at the base of each mesothoracic leg, is a crambid. In addition there are a few species which closely resemble Pyraustinae. *Crambus trisectus, Chilo prejadellus,* and *Dicymolomia julianalis,* together with a large number of unidentified species of Crambus, were examined.

Pyraustinae. The penellipse of crochets which characterizes this subfamily varies in extent from a semicircle to an almost complete ellipse. Other subfamilies are entirely distinct, except a few Crambinae, most of which have biordinal crochets.

Genera of Pyraustinae:

a. Front extending three-fourths, adfrontals nearly or all the way, to the vertical triangle.

   b. Kappa on eighth abdominal segment located directly dorsad of eta; first ocellus much larger than others. *Hellula*

   bb. Kappa on eighth abdominal segment located caudodorsad of eta; first ocellus not much larger than others.

   c. Adfrontals not strongly widened above, their lateral margins rather regularly convergent; head normal in size.

   d. Head not bilobed above, except slightly in some species.

   e. Spiracles elliptical in outline, heavily chitinized, normal in size; body with black pinacula and sometimes black stripes. *Loxostege*

   ee. Spiracles circular in outline, slightly chitinized, very small; body decorated with transverse red stripes. *Eustixia*

   dd. Head conspicuously bilobed above, with the epicranial suture forming a deep groove between the lobes; head black, body marked with conspicuous black and white spots. *Tholeria*

   cc. Adfrontals strongly widened above so that their lateral boundaries appear to be parallel to each other for the ventral three-fourths of their length; head very small. *Cybalomia*

aa. Front extending less than two-thirds of the distance to vertical triangle*; adfrontals not reaching vertical triangle; ocelli subequal in size.

b. Rho on eighth abdominal segment directly dorsad of spiracle.

Hymenia

bb. Rho on eighth abdominal segment cephalodorsad of top of spiracle.

c. Second ocellus about half way between first and third; seta vii usually closest to second ocellus; penellipse more than a semicircle.

d. Front with sides straight or concave.

e. Alpha and rho on ninth abdominal segment in a horizontal line; head not depressed; labrum with a rounded emargination. *Pachyzancla*

ee. Alpha and rho on ninth abdominal segment not in a horizontal line, except in some species in which the labrum has an acute notch.

f. Head very much depressed; labrum with an acute notch.

Desmia

ff. Head not depressed; labrum usually not with an acute notch.

g. Pinacula heavily chitinized, black. *Pyrausta*

gg. Pinacula slightly chitinized, pale. *Phlyctaenia*

dd. Front with sides rather convex throughout their entire length; seta vii closest to third ocellus.

e. Adfrontals conspicuously widened above the front. *Sylepta*

ee. Adfrontals not widened above the front. *Terastia*

cc. Second ocellus much closer to first than to third; seta vii closest to third ocellus; penellipse less than a semicircle.

d. Setae alpha of first abdominal segment more than twice as far apart as each is from beta; body bearing subdorsal longitudinal stripes or dotted areas; subdorsal pinacula heavily chitinized. *Evergestis*

dd. Setae alpha of first abdominal segment not more than one and a half times as far apart as each is from beta.

e. Alpha directly dorsad of rho on eighth abdominal segment.

f. Labrum very broad and short, shallowly but acutely emarginate; head spotted. *Dichogama*

ff. Labrum normal, with a rounded emargination; head unicolorous.

g. Thoracic legs and abdominal prolegs short and often stout.

---

*Except sometimes in *Evergestis* which may fall in "a".

h. Head compressed, retractile, one and a half times as
long as prothorax.   *Diaphania*

hh. Head not compressed, not noticeably retractile,
smaller than prothorax.   *Asciodes*

gg. Thoracic legs and abdominal prolegs long and slender;
head not compressed, not greater than prothorax in
height.

h. Head higher than broad; body pale.   *Pantographa*

hh. Head broader than high; body marked with black
spots.   *Epicorsia*

ee. Alpha located much farther cephalad than rho on eighth
abdominal segment.   *Paradosis*

The following species were examined:

Hellula undalis	*Loxostege sticticalis*
Phlyctaenia extricalis	*L. mancalis*
P. tertialis	*L. maclurae*
Eustixia pupula	*Tholeria reversalis*
Cybalomia belialis	*Hymenia perspectalis*
Pachyzancla bipunctalis	*Desmia funeralis*
Pyrausta penitalis	*Sylepta fluctuosalis*
P. cingulata	*Terastia meticulosalis*
P. thestealis	*Evergestis dyaralis*
Dichogama redtenbacheri	*E. rimosalis*
Diaphania nitidalis	*Asciodes gordialis*
D. quadristigmalis	*Pantographa limata*
D. sibillalis	*Epicorsia mellinalis*
Paradosis flegia	

Nymphulinae. All the aquatic Pyralidoidea of America are included in this subfamily. The resulting structural modifications cause
some difficulty in studying the chaetotaxy of the larvae. The few species
with tracheal gills are easily identified, for no other insects possess both
gills and prolegs with crochets.

Alpha is located near rho but the relative position of the two varies
in different genera. Elophila and Nymphula differ from Scopariinae
and Crambinae in the fact that the setae beta on segment 9 are three
times as far apart as each is from alpha of that side, alpha being nearly
in a direct line between beta and rho and close to each of them. On the
other hand Geschna has the setae beta located near the dorsomeson as
usual but differs from other Pyralidoidea in the position of alpha, which
is directly cephalad of and close to rho. The kappa group on segment 9
is rather difficult to locate in this subfamily. The species examined
were:

Nymphula obscuralis, N. obliteralis,
Geschna (Nymphula) cannalis
Elophila lemnata

Scopariinae. No American species of this subfamily have been seen. *Scoparia crataegella* has kappa and eta of the prothorax forming a vertical line; kappa and eta of the abdomen forming a horizontal line; alpha of segment 9 close to and cephalodorsad of rho; beta of segment 9 close to dorsomeson and located farther caudad than alpha and rho; kappa and mu absent from this segment; crochets biordinal, not triordinal, in a complete circle. Otherwise similar to Crambinae.

FAMILY ORNEODIDAE

Head mainly horizontal in position, smaller than prothorax, smooth; front extending about two-thirds of the distance to the vertical triangle; adfrontals indistinct; first five ocelli arranged in an arc, with the sixth behind the fifth; no secondary setae present. Body pale, bearing primary setae only; shape cylindrical; intersegmental incisions moderate. Prothorax with alpha, gamma and epsilon in a transverse row, beta and delta normal and rho behind and slightly below level of epsilon; Kappa group bisetose; Pi group bisetose; mesothorax with kappa closer to eta than to theta, otherwise normal. Abdomen with alpha above level of beta, rho dorsad of spiracle, kappa and eta adjacent, mu present; Pi group consisting of one seta on segments 1, 7, and 8 and of three setae on segments 2 to 6 inclusive; segments 9 and 10 damaged in material examined. Spiracles circular, slightly larger on prothorax than on other segments, located farther dorsad on segment 8 than on segments 1 to 7. Prolegs short, present on segments 3, 4, 5, and 6, bearing a complete circle of uniordinal crochets.

The family contains but one species, *Orneodes hexadactyla*. It will be seen from the description that the structure is essentially that of a pyralid, being distinguished from all other micros, except some Pterophoridae, by the bisetose Kappa group of the prothorax. Galleria is the only genus of Pyralididae which ever has uniordinal crochets and in it the body is fusiform, the size large, and the Pi group on the mesothorax is bisetose.

FAMILY PTEROPHORIDAE

Variations in the characters of the Plume-moth larvae are so numerous that some difficulty may be met with in placing some of the species. In practice, however, one soon learns to know the long, stemlike prolegs, regardless of the number of setae or crochets. (See Fig. 61.) No other caterpillars possessing verrucae and secondary setae have prolegs of this shape, altho a few lower micros with primary setae show similar structures. All of the latter, however, have a trisetose Kappa group on the prothorax while that of the Pterophoridae is bisetose as in other Pyralidoidea. The species examined were *Pterophorus elliottii*, *Oxyptilus periscelidactylus*, *Platyptilia cosmodactyla* of America, and *Pterophorus microdactylus* and *Platyptilia rhododactylus* of Europe. In all of these verrucae are developed, except in *Pterophorus microdactylus* where the setae are as in Pyralididae.

SUPERFAMILY ZYGAENOIDEA

We begin the discussion of this superfamily with forms which have reached the point of the appearance of well developed verrucae and mesoserial crochets. The verrucae later become more strongly modified and the crochets peculiarly specialized. Another step and the crochets are wholly lost, while the armature includes forms of scoli found in no other larvae. The end of the process is seen in such a slug caterpillar as *Prolimacodes*, with the head minute and completely retracted, and the body smooth and almost spherical, bearing no processes of any kind except three pairs of minute thoracic legs.

No larvae of the families Chalcosidae and Dalceridae have been seen.

Family Pyromorphidae

Pyromorphid larvae form one of the earliest steps in the evolution of a typical Micro into a slug caterpillar. The Pterophoridae include the most plausible connecting links to the generalized types. The following characters show the close relation to Megalopygidae:

Head small, retractile, caudal half slightly chitinized; labrum with a small emargination; ocelli all similar in size, the fifth not set as far caudad of the fourth as in most caterpillars; primary setae only. Body cylindrical, with large flat verrucae. Prothorax with numerous setae on cervical shield, verruca of the Kappa group large; mesothorax and metathorax each with the verrucae of the Kappa group and of the Pi group forming single verrucae and with three verrucae dorsad of them on each side. Abdomen (Fig. 59) with verruca alpha fused with beta, and rho and the verruca of the Kappa group well developed; mu present; Pi group consisting of one or two verrucae. Prolegs present on segments 3, 4, 5, 6, and 10, each with crochets in a uniordinal mesoseries.

Triprocris is a western genus ranging from Mexico to Colorado and including eight species. *T. smithsonianus*, the one examined, has a large subventral eversible gland or fleshy protuberance on the prothorax associated with Pi, and two verrucae, the smaller cephalad of the larger, present between the proleg and the ver lca of the Kappa group on abdominal segments 2 to 6; there is also a similar pair of verrucae on segment 7 but none on 8. The dorsomeson is marked by a dark line.

Harrisina and Acoloithus have the prothoracic protuberance but there is only one verruca between that of the Kappa group and the proleg on segments 2 to 6 and none on 7 or 8. *Harrisina americana* is rather common in the eastern states, feeding on grape and Virginia Creeper. The larva is pale except for the dark reddish verrucae. *H. metallica* of Texas and Arizona has a broad dark red lateral line running just above the spiracle, and transverse intersegmental stripes. The otherwise pale body of *H. brillians,* from the same region, is gaily decked with two broad reddish transverse stripes, the cephalic covering parts of the last thoracic and first two abdominal segments and the caudal extending from the verrucae of the sixth abdominal segment to those of the seventh. In addition the prothorax, mesothorax, and fourth and eighth abdominal segments bear narrow transverse vittae.

Acoloithus falsarius is pale, but obscurely dotted above. Other species of *Acoloithus* and *Harrisina* are very similar in the larval stage. The adults in this division of the family will have to be studied more carefully before the larvae can be correctly placed. Apparently some of the species have dimorphic larvae.

The larva of *Pyromorpha dimidiata* is dull, dark-colored. The prothorax does not bear a subventral protuberance; the verruca mu is present on the first seven abdominal segments but is not associated with a second verruca as in Triprocris.

FAMILY EPIPYROPIDAE.

The two species of this family, one Asiatic, *Epipyrops anomala,* and one American, *E. barberiana,* are anomalous caterpillars with a parasitic habit. The body is in the form of a depressed hemisphere, the head retractile within the first segments. Both thoracic and abdominal legs are present, the claws of the former being peculiar in that they bear a long tooth at the base. The crochets are in a complete circle and, altho uniordinal, are slightly irregular in position and length, their form being degenerate. Secondary setae are sparsely scattered over the entire body. The small head, stout body, and secondary setae indicate an affinity with the Zygaenoidea but reduction has taken a different direction than in Cochlidiidae. There is no sign of verrucae and the crochets are in a complete circle, an arrangement lost even in the Pyromorphidae.

FAMILY MEGALOPYGIDAE.

This family forms one of the important links in the Zygaenoidea, standing between the Zygaenidae themselves and the Cochlidiidae. Its members are particularly interesting as transition forms and their structure is the clue to the peculiarities of the slug caterpillars.

Head and cephalic part of prothorax retractile; head very small, slightly chitinized caudad of the fork of the epicranial suture; epicranium marked by a transverse line between apical and occipital areas, the former more heavily chitinized; labrum with a small mesal emargination; fourth and fifth ocelli much larger than others, sixth ocellus at a distance from first five; head setae sparse and slender.

Body thickened in the middle, small at the ends, fusiform; verrucae large but flat. Prothorax with one large verruca dorsad of spiracle, one small one (Kappa) in front of it, and two (Pi) at base of leg; mesothorax with three verrucae, Beta group, rho, and epsilon, above that of the Kappa group, Beta the largest; two verrucae forming Pi group at base of leg; metathorax with only two verrucae above that of the Kappa group, epsilon and rho being fused; otherwise similar to mesothorax. Abdomen with verrucae alpha and beta coalesced, kappa and eta coalesced; Pi group consisting of one verruca on segment 1 and of three around the base of each of the six pairs of ventral prolegs. Spiracles all circular, those of prothorax largest. Prolegs present on segments 2 to 7 and 10, those on 3, 4, 5, 6 bearing uniordinal crochets in two groups, cephalic group the smaller; these two groups form an angulated mesoseries in most cases but in one genus they are distinctly separated.

Carama cretata. Fifth ocellus as far from fourth as from first; two groups of crochets distinctly separated; verrucae each consisting of a thick group of short stiff setae and a few long slender ones.

Lagoa crispata has the fifth ocellus close to the fourth, the two groups of crochets contiguous and the verrucae each consisting of a few stiff setae and a great many slender ones. All the setae are subequal in length.

Megalopyge opercularis has the fifth ocellus rather distant from the fourth and the crochets and verrucae as in Lagoa. The dorsal setae of the ninth and tenth abdominal segments, however, are twice as long as those of the first eight segments and form a conspicuous tail.

FAMILY COCHLIDIIDAE.

In tables it is rather difficult to separate the slug caterpillars from the larvae of other Holometabola, but in nature the thick, short, fleshy body and the minute thoracic legs will distinguish these forms from all others. It should be remembered that there are no prolegs but that the thoracic legs are always present. The different genera seem to have little in common except the small retractile form of head. The armature has developed from verrucae, altho it often includes scolus-like structures. Some of the genera are entirely smooth.

A synopsis of the American species of this family is given as the conclusion of a series of papers by Dyar in 1899. It will be found in Jour. N. Y. Ent. Soc. 8, 1899, p. 235.

FAMILY LACOSOMIDAE.

Head rugose, wider than prothorax and much higher, with vertex on same level as dorsum of body but with ventral portion produced as far as the thoracic legs are long; ocelli all rather close together; labrum with a small notch; no secondary setae. Body widest at proleg-bearing segments, sometimes fusiform. Prothorax with epsilon below alpha and gamma, rho moved forward to a position near it; Kappa group bisetose. Mesothorax as usual. Alpha of abdomen nearer dorsomeson than beta on segments 1 to 9; kappa and eta adjacent; Pi group consisting of two to three setae on segments 1 and 2, four to eight setae on each proleg; two setae on segments 7 and 8, and one seta on segment 9. Prolegs present on segments 3 to 6 and 10, each of the five pairs bearing a biordinal complete circle of crochets.

Cicinnus melsheimeri has seta iv of the head enlarged and spatulate, its base as large as an ocellus; each proleg has six to eight setae on its cephalolateral surface; the anal segment is depressed; and the body is much thicker in the middle than at the ends.

Lacosoma chiridota has seta iv of the head normal, its base much smaller than an ocellus; each proleg bears four setae on its cephalolateral surface; the anal segment is scarcely depressed and the body is only slightly thickened in the proleg region. *L. arizonica* has not been seen.

FAMILY NOLIDAE.

Systematists differ greatly in placing this family. Hampson, in 1900, makes Nolinae one of the subfamilies of Arctiidae, which he considers the highest family of the entire order. A few years later Dyar includes the group in his Tineoidea, close to Cochlidiidae, Megalopygidae, etc. The latter position is based on the presence of but one verruca (Kappa) between Rho and mu, caudoventrad of the spiracle on the abdomen (Fig. 60), it being assumed that this verruca arose from a coalescence of kappa and eta. As many Acronyctinae have verruca kappa reduced to a single seta or even absent (Figs. 65 and 66) this condition does not seem sufficient to prove conclusively the position of the group.

Head smooth, smaller than prothorax, partially retractile, bearing primary setae only; front wider than high, not reaching half way to vertical triangle; labrum notched to about one-third its depth; sixth ocellus usually at a considerable distance from upper five which are in a semicircle enclosing seta vii; seta v rather closely associated with first ocellus (Fig. 86). Body cylindrical, bearing verrucae but no secondary setae except on prolegs. Prothorax with a large shield on which the dorsal verrucae are united; mesothorax bearing four verrucae on each side in a transverse row. Abdomen with the verrucae of the Beta, Rho, and Kappa groups present on the first nine segments; in addition segments 1, 2, 3, and 7 have mu and Pi in the form of small verrucae, and sigma a single seta; segments 4, 5, and 6 (Fig. 60) possess mu, but the setae of the Pi group are scattered over the proleg and united with sigma; on segments 8 and 9 mu is wanting but Pi is present. Prolegs are present on segments 4, 5, 6, and 10, only; crochets always biordinal, in a mesoseries.

The various species differ in the development of the verrucae, the positions of the ocelli, and the coloration. Owing to lack of material it is not possible to diagnose genera at the present time, especially as the differences which do exist overlap generic limits. The ocellar groups of two species are shown in Figs. 86 and 87.

MACROHETEROCERA

SUPERFAMILY BOMBYCOIDEA

FAMILY EPIPLEMIDAE

Head about as high as wide, slightly bigibbous, usually minutely rugose; front extending about half way to vertical triangle; labrum moderately emarginate; no secondary setae. Prothorax bearing a dorsal plate with the setae in the usual positions, epsilon cephaloventrad of rho above spiracle; Kappa and Pi groups each consisting of two setae; mesothorax and metathorax normal. Abdomen (Fig. 62) with kappa and eta at about the same level below the spiracle, close together on segments 1 to 3, farther apart on segments 4 to 8; mu always associated with lambda, an additional subprimary; Pi group represented by one seta on segment 1, two setae on segment 2, four setae on the prolegs of segments 3 to 6, and one seta on segments 7 to 9; segment 9 with alpha below level of beta and as far from it as from rho, Kappa and Pi groups each represented by one seta. Prolegs with the planta semicircular, the band of crochets so curved as to be similar to a penellipse, crochets biordinal. Spiracles elliptical, those of the prothorax and abdominal segment 8 twice as high and wide as those of the other abdominal segments.

Four genera of this family are found in North America, only two of them occurring east of the Rocky Mountains. In *Callizzia inornata,* setae rho, kappa, and eta on segment 8 are about twice as far from the enlarged spiracle of that segment as the spiracle is high, and the coloration consists principally of a dark band through the setae rho, shading off to lighter brown above; the ventral half of the body is pale; the head is smooth and shining. In *Calledapteryx dryopterata,* setae rho, kappa, and eta are all closer to the spiracle than the spiracle is high, the coloration is paler and more indefinite, and the head is often coarsely rugose.

FAMILY GEOMETRIDAE.

Limits of time and space forbid a discussion of the "loopers" or "inch-worms". There seems to be sufficient variation in the armature, setae, and number and position of prolegs to warrant the belief that a separation of the genera is possible. As no other family has the pro-

legs of any of its members reduced to two pairs, one ventral and one
anal, no difficulty need be encountered in placing the great majority of
the species in the proper family.   The additional rudimentary prolegs
of Brephos, Anisopteryx, and a few other genera are likely to cause
confusion.   The larvae of this family are distinguished by the following
characters, some of them possessed by other families, but when taken
together, completely diagnostic of the Geometridae.

Body usually slender and cylindrical but sometimes bearing humps,
processes, and protuberances of various kinds and shapes; only primary
setae present above the level of the spiracle, but below eta subprimaries
always found, varying in number from one, lambda, to many, covering
the lateral half of the proleg.   Prolegs of abdominal segments 3, 4,
and 5 absent or, in a few cases, rudimentary; crochets biordinal, arranged in a mesoseries.   (Fig. 63.)

FAMILY PLATYPTERYGIDAE.

Head about as high as wide, obscurely bigibbous; no secondary setae
present.   Prothorax with epsilon and rho much farther cephalad than in
most Macrolepidoptera, Kappa group consisting of two setae.   Pi group
usually consisting of several setae borne on a lateral fleshy protuberance;
mesothorax with all setae above spiracular level normal; below eta five
or six setae are present in various arrangements, usually two on a level
with mu of the abdomen and several in a group at the base of the leg
forming the Pi group; metathorax similar.   Abdomen with alpha and
beta separate, epsilon and rho separate dorsad of spiracle, kappa caudad of spiracle, and eta below; mu present; three setae at base of proleg and three more on its lateral surface; segment 9 various.   Setae
usually borne on small chalazae, with great variation on ventral half of
body, tho never very numerous.   Prolegs of segments 3 to 6 with the
planta circular, the crochets biordinal or uniordinal, arranged in a
pseudocircle (Fig. 97), with the mesoseries extending about half way
round the proleg, the lateral series shorter, with smaller crochets, not
continuous with the mesoseries; anal prolegs wanting.   Suranal plate
terminating in an acute process (Fig. 89).   Spiracles elliptical, those of
prothorax about twice as large as those of abdominal segments.

The genera, representatives of all four of which are in the U. S.
National Museum, may be distinguished by the various shapes and sizes
of the processes bearing the setae.

Eudeilinea.   Metathorax cylindrical, smooth above; head not
bicornute; crochets uniordinal.   The family Auzatidae, including in
America only the single species of this genus, *E. herminiata,* is considered distinct from Platypterygidae in Comstock's ''Manual for the
Study of Insects.''   The absence of a chalaza from the metathorax of

the larvae and the lack of secondary setae seem strongly to favor this view.

Falcaria. This contains the single species, *F.bilineata.* It has a pair of chalazae on the mesothorax, another on the metathorax, and another on the second abdominal segment. The Pi group on the prothorax is borne on a conspicuous protuberance, about as long as the thoracic legs. The setae beta of segment 9 are closer together than setae alpha.

Drepana. Chalazae as in Falcaria. Prothoracic protuberance not as long as the thoracic legs. The setae beta on segment 9 are farther apart than setae alpha. *D. arcuata* from the eastern states is dark red above and bears a pair of dorsal chalazae on the first abdominal segment. *D. siculifer* from the Pacific coast is paler and segment 1 is without chalazae.

Oreta. Metathorax bearing a single corniculum on dorsomeson Head prominently bicornute. *Oreta rosea* was the only species examined.

FAMILY BOMBYCIDAE.

Bombyx mori, the only species of the Bombycidae in North America, shows considerable resemblance to a sphingid but scarcely any similarity to the Saturnioidea, with which it is often placed. The setae are so reduced as to be of little value in identification. The caudal horn is present. Other characters are given in the table for the separation of families.

FAMILY LASIOCAMPIDAE.

The larvae of the lasiocampids are usually made conspicuous by their large size, long setae and bright colors. They are common leaf-eating caterpillars and some do considerable damage. The number of setae over the entire head and body makes technical description and location in tables difficult.

Head smaller than body, often retractile, usually depressed; secondary setae numerous on all parts; labrum notched in most species to about one half its depth, notch sometimes continued as a groove which does not, however, extend to the clypeus. Prothorax usually bearing one or two blunt, fleshy protuberances just above the legs, sometimes reduced to mere swellings; other segments of body sometimes bearing similar swellings. Protuberances always present when the body setae are short and sparse, otherwise the setae are extremely irregular in length, ranging from very short to as long as the body is wide; setae never in pencils or verricules or on verrucae or scoli. Sometimes a gibbosity or blunt horn is found on segment 8 on the dorsomeson. Prolegs present on segments 3, 4, 5, 6, and 10 as usual; crochets biordinal, arranged in a mesoseries.

The genera may be distinguished as follows:

a. Body not bearing prominent lateroventral protuberances.
  b. Body depressed; head depressed, partially retractile. *Heteropacha*
  bb. Body cylindrical; dorsal setae as long as lateral setae.
    c. Head black, with epicranial suture inconspicuous; labral notch
      always deep.   *Malacosoma*
    cc. Head with epicranial suture forming a conspicuous yellow
      inverted Y on the black background, or with pale lateral areas;
      labrum sometimes only shallowly emarginate at apex.
            Gloveria

aa. Body bearing conspicuous lateroventral protuberances, longest on
  prothorax, where they are proleg-like; longest setae situated on these
  protuberances, dorsal setae very short or absent.
  b. Body segments each with a pair of verruca-like swellings on the
    dorsum, those of segment 8 subequal in size to those of other
    segments.   *Tolype*
  bb. Body segments without paired dorsal verruca-like swellings,
    but a short fleshy dorsal horn on segment 8. *Epicnaptera*

Heteropacha rileyana is small and onisciform in shape. It is more closely related to Tolype than to Malacosoma, but the fleshy processes are reduced.

Of Malacosoma, eight species are found in the United States. Most of them are large and cylindrical caterpillars with long setae. There is considerable variation in color. A table of the species has been written by Dyar and will be found in the Canadian Entomologist, 25, 1893, p. 43.

Gloveria arizonensis and *G. howardi*, the only species of this genus examined, overlap Malacosoma in most characters. In *arizonensis* the labrum has a very shallow emargination, while in the other species it is notched to about one-half its depth.

Tolype velleda has the body very much depressed and this appearance is increased by the long setae between the spiracles and prolegs. The venter is almost naked. The setae are grayish brown and the body is inconspicuously marked except for a dorsal black transverse vitta on the metathorax. The dorsal metathoracic verrucae are more prominent than those of any other segment. *Tolype laricis* is similar, except that the verrucae of the metathorax are not increased in size.

Epicnaptera americana is a large species with the setae reduced in size in the later stages. The prothoracic protuberances on each side are very large.

FAMILY EUPTEROTIDAE

This European family includes the American genus Apatelodes, usually but incorrectly listed with Notodontidae. Numerous genera of the family are found in Europe and Asia.

Head about as high as body, not retractile, about as wide as high; labral notch deep, either reaching two-thirds distance to clypeus or continued as a groove which reaches clypeus; front extending about one-third the distance to the vertical triangle; head densely covered with secondary setae, thrown back so that the mouth parts are directed almost cephalad. Body cylindrical, covered with numerous secondary setae, some short, others much longer, no fleshy protuberances or verrucae present; mediodorsal setae usually grouped into a distinct tuft on each segment, sometimes forming long pencils; setae longer in thoracic than in abdominal region and on ventral part of abdomen than on dorsal. Prolegs present on segments 3, 4, 5, 6, and 10 as usual, those of the anal segment similar to the others; crochets biordinal.

Apatelodes torrefacta has the body densely setiferous, the setae long and soft. Conspicuous pencils are borne on the dorsomeson of the last two thoracic and the eighth abdominal segments. The labrum is emarginate to about two-thirds its depth. *A. angelica* is more quietly colored, being a grayish brown. The setae of the dorsomeson are comparatively short, but grouped in a small tuft on each body segment; no pencils are present. The labrum is emarginate about half its depth and the notch is continued to the clypeus in the form of a shallow groove.

FAMILY LIPARIDAE

The caterpillars of the tussock moth family may be divided into two groups, those of the first resembling arctians, those of the second having an individuality all their own. Both divisions bear dorsal eversible glands on abdominal segments 6 and 7.

The genera of the first group have typical verrucae, the arrangement as in Arctiidae and Acronycta, except that there are three verrucae above the Kappa group on the mesothorax and metathorax. The usual variation in regard to kappa on the abdomen is to be observed, tho the fusion with rho in *Porthetria dispar* is unique. The separation or contiguity of alpha and beta is merely incidental to the amount of development of these verrucae and the area they occupy.

Group two is a contrast to the commonplace larvae of the first division, being bizarre in color and armature. The long pencils are composed of peculiar setae with spurs much longer near the tip than at the base. This gives a clavate appearance, altho the seta is not itself swollen. The locations of these "clavate-plumed setae" are good taxonomic characters.

Genera of Liparidae:

a. Body bearing tufted setae but no long pencils or dense verricules.
  b. Abdominal segments bearing a single large verruca, eta, below
    spiracle, with a very small one, mu, behind it; verruca rho fused
    with kappa dorso-caudad of the spiracle; verruca alpha on ab-
    domen distinct, tho small.   *Porthetria*
  bb. Abdominal segments bearing two large verrucae below spiracle,
    mu directly below eta; kappa, when present, distinct, behind
    spiracle; verruca alpha fused with beta.
    cc. Verruca kappa present and distinct, tho small; body bearing
      some very feathery setae.   *Gynaephora*
    cc. Verruca kappa absent or indistinct; setae echinulate but not
      feathery.   *Euproctis*
aa. Body bearing a pair of long pencils of setae on prothorax and a
  mesal pencil on segment 8.
  b. First four abdominal segments bearing dense dorsal verricules
    very different from verrucae of other segments.
    c. Clavate-plumed setae present on all or nearly all segments.
                              (In part)   *Olene*
    cc. Clavate-plumed setae present only in the tufts of the prothorax
      and eighth abdominal segment and sometimes on the second
      abdominal segment.   *Hemerocampa*
                                  Notolophus
  bb. First four abdominal segments bearing verrucae similar to those
    of other segments.   (In part)   *Olene*

Porthetria includes a single species, the Gipsy moth, *P. dispar.*

Euproctis chrysorrhea is the Browntail moth and is the only species of this European genus as yet introduced into America.

The characters given for Gynaephora in the synopsis refer to *G.
rossii,* the larva of which differs greatly from *G. groenlandica.* The
latter species occurs only in the Arctics.

Olene achatina differs from other members of the second group in
the absence of verricules on the first four abdominal segments. The
setae densely cover all parts of the body. Clavate-plumed setae are
present only on the prothorax. *O. leucophaea, O. pini* Dyar, and *O.
plagiata* are more similar to the common Tussock moth.

Hemerocampa and Notolophus overlap and the larvae can not be
distinguished. *N. antiqua* differs from the others in the presence of
clavate-plumed setae on abdominal segment 2. The others may be separated by the table given by Dyar in Psyche, 7, 1893, p. 421.

Family Thyatiridae

Head vertical, wider than high; front small; adfrontals distinct; no secondary setae; labrum usually notched to about two-thirds its depth, sides of notch parallel. Body cylindrical, not bearing secondary setae; primary and subprimary setae arranged as described for Epiplemidae except that the Pi group on the prolegs consists of three setae only and of at least two setae on segments 1, 2, 7, and 8. Ventral prolegs bearing biordinal crochets in a curved mesoseries; anal prolegs reduced to one-half or two-thirds size of ventral.

Habrosyne rectangulata has the head shining and the Pi group on the mesothorax and metathorax bisetose. In *H. scripta* the head is more or less dull and minutely rugose, the dorsal half of the abdomen bears diagonal stripes, and the Pi group on the last two thoracic segments is unisetose.

Pseudothyatira expultrix and *P. cymatophoroides* each show a dull and rugose head and unmarked body. The Pi group is bisetose on each thoracic segment.

Family Notodontidae

Larvae of this family are usually identified at a glance by their peculiar decoration and shapes. A student of the larval stage can not accede to Hampson's view that the arctians, noctuids, and syntomids are specialized modifications of the notodontian type, or that Notodontidae are a generalized family. All the species have secondary setae on the sides of the prolegs and specialized anal prolegs, thus departing widely from the generalized condition retained by Noctuidae.

Many species of the subfamily Notodontinae will trace to Noctuidae in any tables hitherto published. The setiferous prolegs will serve to distinguish in most of these cases. Other characters are given in the table for the separation of the families. The subfamilies may be recognized by the following key:

a. Body bearing numerous secondary setae, obscuring primary ones; anal prolegs not increased in size.
    b. Head bearing numerous short, fine, secondary setae; abdominal segments 1 and 8 often bearing conspicuous dorsal cornicula.
                                   Melalophinae
    bb. Head without secondary setae; dorsal cornicula never present.
                                     Pygaerinae
aa. Body bearing only primary setae above level of prolegs; anal prolegs usually elongated.
    b. Dorsum of thorax consisting of a broad flattened triangle with conspicuous lateral prothoracic and mesal metathoracic angles; anal prolegs long; head small, partially retractile.   Cerurinae

bb. Dorsum of thorax not flattened nor triangular; anal prolegs not greatly elongated; head usually as large as prothorax.

NOTODONTINAE

Melalophinae. This subfamily includes the one genus Melalopha (Ichthyura). The six species may be distinguished by the characters given by Packard, (1895).

Pygaerinae. The larvae of Datana are well known in all parts of the United States. As the colors change at each molt the species are hard to separate. Packard gives a key to them which may be used with more or less success, and his figures are invaluable. He was acquainted with the larvae of all described species except *robusta, modesta,* and *chiriquensis.* *D. robusta* is very similar to *D. contracta* but the stripes are dark brown instead of creamy white and the prothoracic shield is black instead of yellow in the last instar.

Cerurinae. Two genera, Harpyia and Cerura, whose larvae are very similar, compose this group. The long stemapoda, or modified anal prolegs, distinguish them at a glance from other Notodontidae. In *Cerura scitiscripta* the metathorax has a single median prominence, and in *C. occidentalis* there is a bifurcate one. The metathorax of the species of Harpyia is without prominences. All have a dorsal reddish somewhat broken vitta running the entire length of the body and reaching in some places as far ventrad as the spiracle. In *H. cinerea* this vitta is wanting on the metathorax but in the other two species it is continuous from thorax to abdomen. Its lateral margins are convex on the mesothorax of *H. scolopendrina* and concave in *H. borealis.*

Notodontinae. At first glance the genera which are grouped together under this name seem rather heterogeneous. The wing venation of the adults is as various as the form of the larvae. Nevertheless a logical separation of Gluphisia and the Heterocampinae seems almost impossible. The former is very closely related to some of the Notodontinae as Packard limited the group. The species of Heterocampa form a series of transition stages from typical notodontians to the peculiarly specialized larvae of Schizura and Hyparpax. This is in striking contrast to the distinct separation of the Pygaerinae and the Ichthyurinae from other members of the family. The long stemapoda in early stages of Fentonia (Macrurocampa) seem to indicate that even Cerura and Hayrpia should be included here. Other structures, however, make the line of separation distinct. The various genera may be distinguished by means of the following synopsis. The comparative clause in the first division is due to the peculiar dorsal series of gibbosities of Nerice, a genus which clearly belongs in the second group.

Genera of Notodontinæ:

a. First abdominal segment bearing a higher dorsal gibbosity than second, gibbosity usually either bifurcate or bearing a pair of cornicula.
  b. Dorsal corniculum of segment 8 single, that of segment 1 obscurely
     bifurcate.   *Ianassa*
  bb. Dorsal corniculum of segments 1 and 8 distinctly bifurcate.
    c. Segments 4 and 5 not gibbous above; color between humps on
       segments 1 and 8 mainly in a single elliptical patch; labrum
       notched to two-thirds its depth.   *Hyparpax*
    cc. Segments 4 and 5 usually gibbous above; color between seg-
       ments 1 and 8 never in a distinct elliptical patch; labrum not
       notched to two-thirds its depth.   *Schizura*
aa. First abdominal segment not bearing a higher dorsal gibbosity than
    second; gibbosity, when present, neither bifurcate nor bearing a
    pair of cornicula.
  b. Segment 8 bearing a distinct dorsal hump or horn or pair of cor-
     nicula.
    c. Dorsal processes of segment 8 slender, horn-like.
      d. Horn single, similar to the caudal horn of a sphingid.
                                                                Pheosia
      dd. Horns paired, slender and sharply pointed.   *Ptilodon*
    cc. Dorsal hump of segment 8 broad, not horn-like.
      d. Segment 2 conspicuously gibbous above.
        e. Abdomen bearing high dorsal gibbosities on eight segments.
                                                                Nerice
        ee. Abdomen bearing dorsal humps on not more than five seg-
           ments.   (In part) *Hyperaeschra*
      dd. Segment 2 not gibbous above.
        e. Segment 8 swollen and discolored over entire dorsal half;
           coloration mainly a series of longitudinal stripes.
                                                               Symmerista
        ee. Segment 8 not swollen over entire dorsal half.
          f. Anal prolegs short and rounded; coloration in indefinite
             transverse stripes.   *Odontosia*
          ff. Anal prolegs usually elongate.
            g. Head bearing a pair of dark dorsal spots.   *Ellida*
            gg. Head unicolorous.
              h. Coloration principally a series of conspicuous lon-
                 gitudinal stripes on dorsal half of each segment
                 and rounded spots at base of each leg. *Dasylophia*
              hh. Coloration principally a series of conspicuous trans-

verse stripes on dorsal half and longitudinal stripes on ventral half of body.　　*Didugua*

bb. Segment 8 not bearing a distinct dorsal hump, horn, or gibbosity.
c. Prothorax bearing a pair of dorsal cornicula.
d. Anal prolegs stemapodiform, about as long as body is wide, longer in early stages.　　*Fentonia*
dd. Anal prolegs shorter than body is wide.
e. Head divided by a pair of subvertical lines into three areas, the lateral minutely rugose, the mesal hard and shining.
(In part) *Heterocampa*
ee. Head not divided into three areas.　　*Litodonta*
cc. Prothorax not bearing a pair of dorsal cornicula.
d. Body bearing a distinct lateral line through spiracles or a conspicuous mediodorsal line or both; supraspiracular lines never present.
e. Prothoracic spiracle conspicuous, about twice the height of the abdominal spiracles; second ocellus closer to first than to third.
f. Kappa on segments 5, 6, and 8 separated from the spiracle by a distance equal to about one-half the width of the spiracle.　　(In part) *Hyperaeschra*
ff. Kappa on segments 5, 6, and 8 separated from the spiracle at least as far as the spiracle is wide.　　*Lophodonta*
ee. Prothoracic spiracles about the same size as abdominal spiracles or not more than one and a half times as high.
f. Lateral lines present; second ocellus closer to first than to third; dorsal line double.　　*Gluphisia*
ff. Lateral lines not present; second ocellus closer to third than to first; dorsal line single.　　*Misogada*
dd. Body not bearing lateral lines through spiracles; mediodorsal line when present paralleled by a pair of supraspiracular lines on at least a part of the abdomen.
e. Second and third ocelli closer together than first and second; anal plate usually inconspicuous, all spiracles subequal in size.　　(In part) *Heterocampa*
ee. Second and third ocelli as far apart as first and second; anal plate large, semicircular, nearly as wide as segment 9; spiracles of prothorax much larger than those of abdomen.　　*Nadata*

A discussion of the genera of this, the largest subfamily, would be out of place in a paper of this kind in view of the excellent Monograph by Packard, but as several species have been described since the publication of that work, the following notes are offered:

Ianassa lignicolor, in all except the last stage, is very similar to *Schizura unicornis.* The striped head, with three mesal white marks in a vertical row, will distinguish it, the head of *S. unicornis* being unicolorous red.

Ptilodon americana is called *Odontosia camelina* by Packard. The larva is very distinct from *Odontosia elegans.*

Hyperaeschra shauld apparently be divided into two genera, for the larvae of *H. georgica* and *H. stragula* are very different.

Didugua Druce was erected for the species *argentilinea* Druce, found in Texas. The coloration is distinctive.

The following species of Notodontidae were examined:

Melalopha—all listed species

Datana ministra	*Pheosia dimidiata*
D. *californica*	*Ptilodon americana*
D. *angusii*	*Nerice bidentata*
D. *drexelii*	*Hyperaeschra stragula*
D. *major*	H. *georgica*
D. *palmii*	*Symmerista albifrons*
D. *floridana*	*Odontosia elegans*
D. *perspicua*	*Ellida caniplaga*
D. *robusta*	*Dasylophia anguina*
D. *integerrima*	*Didugua argentilinea* Druce
D. *contracta*	*Fentonia marthesia*
Cerura scitiscripta	*Heterocampa obliqua*
C. *occidentalis*	H. *picta*
Harpyia cinerea	H. *umbrata*
H. *borealis*	H. *manteo*
H. *scolopendrina*	H. *biundata*
Ianassa lignicolor	H. *guttivitta*
Hyparpax aurora	H. *bilineata*
H. *perophoroides*	*Litodonta hydromeli*
Schizura ipomoeae	*Lophodonta ferruginea*
S. *concinna*	L. *angulosa*
S. *semirufescens*	*Gluphisia septentrionalis*
S. *unicornis*	*Misogada unicolor*
S. *apicalis*	*Nadata gibbosa*
S. *badia*	
S. *leptinoides*	
S. *errucata* Dyar	

FAMILY DIOPTIDAE

Phryganidia californica, the only species of this family found in North America, is described and figured by Kellogg and Jackson in

Proc. Cal. Acad. Sci. (2) 5, 1895, p. 563. The larva is noctuiform and
cylindrical with all the usual prolegs present altho the anal ones are
slightly reduced in size. The primary setae are reduced, but easily
located with a lens; secondary setae are present only on the prolegs.
Labrum acutely tho not very deeply notched, as in most Notodontidae.
The cuticular projections of the body are conspicuous under a magnifi-
cation of about two hundred but might be overlooked with a low power
objective. The color is green, with longitudinal black stripes. This
insect is not found east of California.

FAMILY PERICOPIDAE

Head rarely or never bearing secondary setae; thoracic segments
always with sigma large and distinct, close to the coxae; verrucae alpha
and beta of abdomen never contiguous; verruca kappa of abdomen never
reduced, always much lower on segment 7 than on segments 6 and 8;
mesothorax bearing either one or two verrucae above that of the Kappa
group. Otherwise closely similar to Syntomidae (Figs. 67, 68).

The larvae of the American genera and species of this family are
described by Dyar (1914).

FAMILY NYCTEOLIDAE

This family, as such, has been abandoned by Hampson and other
recent lepidopterists. There is certainly no larval justification for its
separation from Noctuidae, altho the position of seta vii on the head
seems to be closer to the second and farther from the third ocellus than
in other noctuid genera. Calling the group "subfamily Sarrothripi-
nae", as Hampson does, seems best to suit the facts of both larval and
adult structure.

FAMILY NOCTUIDAE

The Owlet moths include about one-half of the nearly seven thou-
sand described species of Lepidoptera in North America. A uniform
group of this size naturally presents great problems to the systematist
and takes an amount of time disproportionate even to the size of the
family. By far the majority of the unidentified and misidentified moths
in the museums of the world probably belong to Noctuidae. The monu-
mental work of Hampson, which is still in course of publication, is
doing much to clear up questions of classification; but no amount of
discussion can make a problem of this size easy of solution.

In the larvae the difficulties facing the taxonomist are intensified.
With the exception of half a dozen genera, noctuid larvae are so uniform in structure that one can often compare, part by part, every segment and appendage of larvæ of two species without finding a

difference either of kind or of degree. On the other hand the half-dozen exceptions include species which resemble arctians, lasiocampids, noto-dontids, eupterotids, etc., and which have been distributed by some authors into a variety of families. Naturally it is the latter forms which are most difficult to handle in a synopsis of the entire order but which are easy to separate from each other.

It is not a part of the plan of this paper to enter the subject of the classification of Noctuidae. The range must, however, be considered. Many of the larvae are of such structure that they will not trace to the correct family in any tables hitherto published. It is clear that differ-ent characters must be used in identification according as the setae are primary or secondary or developed into tufts, the crochets biordinal or uniordinal, and the body cylindrical or with prominent humps. We must then divide the family into four groups, of which the first will include nearly all the genera, most of the larvae being of the "cut-worm" type, and the others will be confined to the genera Demas, Pan-thea, Acronycta, Harrisimemna, Agriopodes, Polygrammate, and a few others of minor importance. Larvae of Acronycta will be found in all groups except the first, but species of the other genera mentioned are few in number and individuals rare. These "groups" are purely for convenience and do not constitute a "natural" arrangement.

Group 1. Larvae with primary setae only; prothorax with beta above level of alpha, epsilon associated with rho between delta and spiracle, Kappa and Pi groups each bisetose; mesothorax with alpha associated with beta, epsilon with rho, and kappa with eta, theta sepa-rate, Pi group unisetose; metathorax similar. Abdominal segments 1 to 6 and 8 with alpha above level of beta, rho above level of spiracle; epsilon, when present, smaller, and located cephalodorsad of spiracle, kappa and eta widely separated, mu present, Pi group consisting of three setae on most segments; sigma present; no other setae present except sometimes a few members of the Tau group and sometimes gamma; segment 7 similar, except that kappa is always much lower and closer to eta; segment 9 with alpha, beta, and rho forming a triangle, kappa, eta, mu, pi, and sigma present. Prolegs present on segments 5, 6, and 10, at least, and usually on segments 3 and 4; crochets arranged in a mesoseries, uniordinal except in some Plusiinae and others, in which the crochets are biordinal. This group contains the vast majority of genera but none of the species of Acronycta. (Figs. 17-24, 29-32.)

Group 2. Larvae with well developed verrucae (Figs. 65, 66). Arrangement of tufts similar to that in Arctiidae except that kappa is lower on segment 7 than on segments 6 and 8 (scarcely lower in Cha-radra); in one-fourth of the species kappa is reduced to one or a few setae and is easily overlooked. The crochets of the species of Acronycta are always uniordinal and the full five pairs of prolegs on segments 3 to 6 and 10 are always present. The notch of the labrum is somewhat varied, but, as a rule, is deep, with parallel sides and a rounded bottom. Twenty-two of the forty-two species of Acronycta examined appear to belong in this group, as well as *Charadra deridens, Panthea furcilla, Demas propinquilinea,* the species of Eulonche, Simyra, Polygrammate, Agriopodes, and possibly a few other Acronyctinae.

Group 3. Verrucae obscured by the development of secondary setae. This large number of secondary setae covers all the characters ordinarily used in the identification of noctuids and necessitates a search to find other distinguishing structures. It happens, however, that no other multisetiferous larvae have uniordinal crochets and short prolegs except Datana and Melalopha of the Notodontidae, and these are so distinctive in appearance that there is little danger of confusing Acronycta with them. The parallel-sided notch of the labrum is also distinctive*. Fifteen of the species of Acronycta examined are of this type.

Group 4. Verrucae reduced to single setae or small or indefinite groups of setae in the last instar altho preceded by well developed tufts in earlier stages. In accordance with a well recognized natural law, degeneration of a structure does not result in a condition exactly similar to that from which the structure arose. Thus the reduction of verrucae to single setae almost never causes a complete return to the generalized chaetotaxy. In Lithosiidae this is shown by the double nature of Rho on the abdomen and of Pi on the mesothorax and metathorax, and in Arctiidae by the multisetiferous leg-plate of Doa or the bisetose Pi group on the metathorax of Utetheisa. Both these latter conditions are found in that anomalous, notodontid-like, noctuid genus Harrisimemna. In the Acronyctas, however, the leg-plate seems to have been reduced to three setae and the Pi group on the metathorax to one seta at the same time that alpha, beta, rho, etc., degenerated from verrucae to single setae. It is a strange fact that mu has not followed the same course but retains its multisetiferous condition as a well developed verruca. This is true of all the "single-haired" Acronycta larvae examined, viz., *A. exilis, A. haesitata, A. afflicta,* and *A. funeralis.*

In any synopsis of the larvae for purposes of identification, the four groups must be handled separately in spite of the fact that they have all been derived from the same type. They are listed above in

---

*The labrum of *Acronycta leporina,* which belongs here, is figured by Forbes (1910) as having a shallow notch. This does not agree with the individuals of this species which I have seen nor with any other Noctuidae having numerous secondary setae obscuring the verrucae, so far as I know them.

the order in which they seem to have arisen; first the primary setae, then the development of verrucae, which later became modified either by the addition of numerous secondary setae, or by reduction to almost the primary chaetotaxy again. In the absence of justification in adult structure, it does not seem best to separate the last three groups from the first as a distinct family, as has been done by some previous workers.

FAMILY AGARISTIDAE

This family should meet the same fate as Nycteolidae and be included among the noctuids. The adult structure on which it is based, the clubbed antennae, is so variable that it is hard to limit the group exactly. At the same time the larvae seem to be distinguishable from the Noctuidae only in color, nearly all the species being transversely striped. The one species found east of the Rocky Mountains and north of Florida, *Alypia octomaculata,* may be recognized by the humped eighth abdominal segment, the conspicuous chalazae and the transverse stripes. That is the extreme, however, for the western species form a nearly complete series connecting Alypia with typical Noctuidae. The following species were examined: *Alypia octomaculata, A. langtonii, A. ridingsii, Copidryas gloveri, C. cosyra* Druce, *Androloma mac-cullochii.*

FAMILY ARCTIIDAE

Head smooth, bearing sparse secondary setae or none; front about as wide as high, extending half way to vertical triangle; labrum with a rather wide, shallow emargination, sometimes acute at bottom; ocelli various, the fifth and sixth distant from the others. Body bearing verrucae except in a few reduced genera, *Doa* and *Utetheisa,* in which only primary setae and a few others remain; usual positions of verrucae shown in Figs. 25 to 28, 33, and 34. Verrucae of Beta and Rho groups of mesothorax and metathorax never fused; Kappa of abdominal segments 1 to 8 always distinctly present near spiracle, sometimes, but rarely, slightly lower on segment 7 than on segments 6 and 8; prolegs with uniordinal crochets in a mesoseries, heteroideous in all but a few species. (Fig. 107.)

The author is not satisfied with the following table of the genera but presents it in the hope that it may be of some service. Arctian larvae seem not to possess constant characters of generic value.

a. Verrucae reduced to chalazae bearing single setae.
  b. Head and thorax normal in size; crochets heteroideous.   *Utetheisa*
  bb. Head very small, thorax swollen; crochets homoideous.   *Doa*
aa. Verrucae not reduced, multisetiferous.

b. Subdorsal setae of thorax, at least of metathorax, twice as long as those of middle abdominal segments, usually forming pencils.

  c. Verrucae rho of segment 8 of abdomen each bearing a long pencil of setae; other setae of segments 8 and 9 short.   *Halisidota*

  cc. Verrucae rho of segment 8 not bearing longer setae than verrucae alpha and beta.

    d. Body and setae unicolorous, never black.   *Ammalo*

    dd. Body bearing black, white, and orange colored tufts of setae on the abdomen.   *Euchaetias*

bb. Subdorsal setae of thorax subequal in length to those of abdominal segments.

  c. Labrum notched to at least half its depth.

    d. Each verruca bearing setae of two distinct lengths, the shorter sheared off even, the others fewer, twice as long, irregular in length.   *Hemihyalea*

    dd. Each verruca bearing setae of only one or of irregular lengths.

      e. Cuticula and setae pale; setae sheared off even; size small.   *Eupseudosoma*

      ee. Cuticula and setae very dark, with pale transverse stripes; size very large.   *Ecpantheria*

  cc. Labrum notched to less than half its depth.

    d. Thoracic and caudal abdominal segments bearing setae of a different color from those of proleg-bearing segments.

      e. Setae of four to six middle abdominal segments brown, those of thorax and caudal abdominal segments black.   *Isia*

      ee. Setae of most of abdomen black, those of thorax and end of abdomen brown.   *Platyprepia*

    dd. Thoracic and caudal abdominal segments not bearing setae of a different color from those of proleg-bearing segments.

      e. Each abdominal verruca bearing setae of two contrasting colors, white and black; cuticula unicolorous, without a mediodorsal stripe.

        f. White setae about twice as long as black.   *Arctia*

        ff. White setae about same length as others.   *Ectypia*

      ee. Each abdominal verruca bearing setae of one color only, except when a bright mediodorsal stripe is present.

        f. Verrucae alpha of abdomen about one-third the size of verrucae beta; all verrucae small; setae of segments 8 and 9 not longer than those of other parts of body.

          g. Verrucae kappa of middle abdominal segments partially or entirely above level of lower margin of spiracle.   *Apantesis*

gg. Verrucae kappa of middle abdominal segments well
     below level of spiracle.
  h. All abdominal verrucae below level of beta pale, ver-
     rucae beta black; body marked with longitudinal
     stripes.   *Hyphantria*
  hh. All abdominal verrucae black; setae of verrucae rho
     sometimes forming pencils; no stripes.   *Eubaphe*
ff. Verrucae alpha of abdomen about the same size as ver-
    rucae beta; when distinctly smaller, segments 8 and 9
    bear setae about three times as long as those of other
    segments.
  g. Segments 1, 2, and 7 bearing two verrucae at the same
     level in line with verruca mu of segments 3 to 6;
     setae short; body longitudinally striped.   *Haploa*
  gg. Segments 1, 2, and 7 bearing only one verruca in line
     with verruca mu of segments 3 to 6.
  h. Subdorsal setae of segments 8 and 9 three times as
     long as those of any other segments; over twice as
     long as body is wide.   *Leptarctia*
  hh. Subdorsal setae of segments 8 and 9 usually sub-
     equal in length to those of other segments, never
     twice as long as body is wide.
    i. Labrum very shallowly concave at tip; verrucae
       alpha large, bearing black setae; verrucae beta
       and rho smaller, with white setae.   *Euschausia*
   ii. Labrum rather acutely tho not deeply notched at
       tip; verrucae alpha and beta not of contrasting
       colors.
      j. Verrucae beta of first few abdominal segments
         nearly directly caudad of alpha; verrucae low,
         flat.
        k. Setae very irregular in length, some as long as
           body is wide.   *Hyphoraia*
        kk. Setae sheared off even, never as long as body
           is wide.
          l. Setae of thorax black, those of abdomen
             brown.   *Phragmatobia*
          ll. Setae of thorax and abdomen brown.
                                                 Lerina
      jj. Verrucae beta of first few abdominal segments
          more nearly laterad than caudad of alpha; ver-
          rucae swollen.

k. Dorsum bearing conspicuous transverse yellow and black stripes; verrucae light brown.

Seirarctia

kk. Dorsum not bearing transverse stripes, except sometimes obscurely.

l. Verrucae eta of abdomen twice as broad as verrucae mu, pear-shaped; head black at least in part; body bearing a pale lateral stripe; setae moderately stiff.   *Estigmene*

ll. Verrucae eta of abdomen elongate, with parallel sides, similar to verrucae mu, head usually entirely pale; no lateral stripe of a lighter color than dorsum.

m. Setae light brown or gray, unicolorous, rather soft like fur.   *Diacrisia*

mm. Setae either very dark brown, or black, or variegated in color, always stiff like spines.   *Arachnis*

The following species were examined:

Utetheisa bella
Doa ampla
Halisidota maculata
  H. tessellaris
  H. harrisii
  H. cinctipes
  H. caryae
Ammalo tenera
  A. eglenensis
Euchaetias egle
Hemihyalea edwardsii
Eupseudosoma involutum
Ecpantheria muzina
Isia isabella
Platyprepia virginalis
Arctia caia var. *americana*
Ectypia bivittata
Apantesis virgo
  A. virgo var. *citrinaria*
  A. virguncula
  A. michabo
  A. anna var. *persephone*
  A. arge

A. proxima var. *autholea*
A. nevadensis var. *superba*
A. phyllira
A. figurata
Apantesis (cont'd)
  A. nais
  A. nais var. *radians*
  A. nais var. *phalerata*
Hyphantria cunea
  H. textor
Eubaphe opella
Haploa clymene
  H. colona
  H. lecontei var. *confinis*
  H. confusa
  H. contiguus
Leptarctia californica
Euschausia ingens
  E. argentata
Hyphoraia parthenos
Phragmatobia fuliginosa
Lerina incarnata
Seirarctia echo

Estigmene acraea   *D. latipennis*
    E. congrua   *Arachnis zuni*
Diacrisia rubra   *A. picta*
    D. virginica   *A. confusa* Druce

FAMILY LITHOSIIDAE

The Lithosiidae are arctian in most particulars and some of the larvae are said to be indistinguishable from that family. When vertucae are present, those of the last two thoracic segments are out of line instead of being in definite transverse rows, and usually only one verruca is present between the spiracle and the proleg in addition to the single seta kappa. Of the American forms the writer has seen only species with the armature reduced to single setae and is unable to describe the positions of the verrucae in other genera.

The arrangement of the setae is similar to that in Noctuidae except in two or three particulars. The Pi group on the mesothorax and metathorax is bisetose and Rho on the first six or eight abdominal segments is bisetose. An additional seta is also present near mu on the abdominal segments but the Pi group consists of only three setae. The crochets are homoideous. The labrum is shallowly concave at tip.

Hypoprepia miniata. The three setae composing the Kappa group on the mesothorax placed on one triple chalaza, equidistant from each other and arranged in a horizontal line.

Illice nexa. The three setae composing the Kappa group on the mesothorax not borne on the same chalaza, theta much farther caudad than kappa and eta, which are close together, kappa farther ventrad than the others.

FAMILY SYNTOMIDAE

The Syntomidae are differentiated by the single verruca above that of the kappa group on the last two thoracic segments. The only other similar condition is in one genus of Pericopidae but the position of verruca kappa on segment 7 serves to distinguish the latter from this family (Figs. 67, 68).

Head similar to that of Arctiidae; front almost an equilateral triangle; labrum moderately acute at tip; secondary setae usually present. Body bearing verrucae, usually well developed. Prothorax with verrucae rho rudimentary, but those of kappa and Pi groups large; mesothorax and metathorax with all setae above Kappa group forming a single verruca; Pi normal; sigma small or wanting. Abdominal segments 1 to 8 (Figs. 67, 68) with alpha, beta, rho, kappa, eta, and mu distinct and separate verrucae; kappa often small, in about the same position on segment 7 as on other abdominal segments; Pi group also forming a verruca on segments 1, 2, 7, 8, and 9; verrucae alpha often contiguous on abdomen; secondary setae rare or absent. Thoracic legs well developed; prolegs normal on segments 3, 4, 5, 6, reduced or wanting on 10; crochets uniordinal, either homoideous or heteroideous, arranged in a mesoseries.

Genera of Syntomidae:

a. Verrucae reduced in size, each bearing a few long setae; head bearing long setae; prothoracic legs much reduced.   *Lycomorpha*
aa. Verrucae well developed, at least alpha, beta, and rho consisting of very numerous setae.
  b. Verrucae kappa and eta of abdomen both well developed and bearing numerous setae.
    c. Verrucae kappa of segments 1 and 7 of the abdomen bearing an enlarged group of clavate-plumed setae, tipped with black.
       Cosmosoma
    cc. Verrucae kappa of segments 1 and 7 normal.
      d. Clypeus emarginate at tip, with a median semicircular concavity; front white, adfrontals black; verrucae alpha of first abdominal segment bearing a dark brown pencil.   *Lymire*
      dd. Clypeus not emarginate at tip; front concolorous with adfrontals; verrucae alpha of segment 1 normal.
        e. Secondary setae absent on front; margins of front strongly convex.   *Eucereon*
        ee. Secondary setae of front rather numerous; margins of front nearly straight.   *Ctenucha*
  bb. Verrucae kappa of abdomen abortive, either less than half the size of verrucae eta or both rudimentary.
    c. Verrucae beta of segment 8 bearing a pencil of setae at least twice as long as those of verrucae beta on preceding segments.
      Syntomeida
    cc. Verrucae beta on segments 1 to 9 all similar.
      d. Verrucae alpha and beta of abdomen much better developed than other verrucae, bearing a thick, short verricule on each segment.   *Pseudomya*
      dd. Verrucae alpha and beta of abdomen similar to verrucae rho and kappa and those of the thorax.   *Scepsis*

The following species were examined:

Lycomorpha pholus	*Syntomeida epilais*
Cosmosoma myrodora Dyar (1907)	*S. ipomeae*
Lymire edwardsii	*Pseudomya minima*
Eucereon confine	*Scepsis fulvicollis*
Ctenucha virginica	*Syntomis phegea* of Europe

ILLINOIS BIOLOGICAL MONOGRAPHS

SUPERFAMILY SATURNIOIDEA

Workers differ as to the number of families into which this group should be divided, some defining the Saturniidae and Ceratocampidae, others separating Hemileuca and a few related genera from the former and calling them Hemileucidae. While the writer recognizes these three families, the structure of the larvae compels him to differ from previous workers and to include Automeris and Coloradia in the Hemileucidae. The necessity for this change will be shown in a succeeding paragraph. It is interesting to note that Miss Edna Mosher* found that the pupal characters also relate Automeris more closely to the Hemileucidae than to Samia and Saturnia. Whether specialists will later find that the imagines justify this arrangement remains to be seen.

The difference is emphasized by the basis of separation of the Saturniidae from the Ceratocampidae. Forbes (1905), following Dyar, uses for this purpose the scoli beta on the ninth abdominal segment, which in Ceratocampidae are fused on the dorsomeson. He seems to have overlooked the fact that such a fusion also occurs in Automeris (Fig. 109) and other genera, with the result that these forms trace to Ceratocampidae or Hemileucidae rather than to Saturniidae.

Five types of arrangement of the scoli of segments 8 and 9 are found in the superfamily and four of them are shown in the figures of Plate X. In all five, scoli Rho and Kappa are normal on segment 8, and two similar but more dorsally placed scoli of doubtful homology are found on 9. Dorsad of these four are found the following modifications: (a) a single mediodorsal scolus on 8, none on 9; (b) a subdorsal scolus on each side on 8, none on 9; (c) a mediodorsal scolus on 8, and also one on 9; (d) a mediodorsal scolus and pair of adjacent scoli on 8 and a mesal one only on 9; (e) a mediodorsal scolus on 9, none on 8. The Saturniidae display either (a) (Fig. 108) or (b); the Hemileucidae, including Automeris, are armed as in (c) (Fig. 109); while the Ceratocampidae show either (d) (Fig. 110) or (e) (Fig. 111). It is to be noted that Hemileuca, Pseudohazis, Automeris and Coloradia are more similar to the Ceratocampidae in the armature of these two segments than to the Saturniidae.

The presence of scoli (Figs. 73, 74) distinguishes this superfamily from all others except Nymphalidae and Heliconiidae. In the Saturnioidea, however, the head is never tuberculate nor horned and is always more or less narrowed dorsad; mediodorsal scoli, when present, are confined to segments 8 and 9. The few difficult cases which remain are discussed under Nymphalidae. The position and number of the scoli differ so greatly that an extended diagnosis of the entire group on that

---

*The Classification of the Pupae of the Ceratocampidae and Hemileucidae. Ann. Ent. Soc. Am. 7, 1914, 277-300.

basis is impossible. They are never absent in American species so far as examined, but in the last stage of the European *Aglia tau,* only great dorsal gibbosities remain to show that the recent form has descended from saturnian ancestors.

Beta on the first eight abdominal segments of members of this superfamily is either represented by a single seta or is wanting. The eighth segment of Ceratocampidae is an exception, for here there is a pair of small scoli caudad of the large mediodorsal scolus alpha.

The crochets are always biordinal and arranged in a mesoseries. (Fig. 106). The anal prolegs are usually flattened laterocaudally and, with the anal plate, form a triangular pyramid.

Families of Saturnioidea:

a. Ninth abdominal segment not bearing a scolus on the dorsomeson; scoli never profusely branched; mediodorsal scolus of segment 8, when present, never associated with a pair of smaller scoli latero-caudad of it (Fig. 108).   SATURNIIDAE
aa. Ninth abdominal segment bearing a scolus on the dorsomeson (Figs. 109, 110, 111).
  b. Scoli alpha of mesothorax scarcely longer than abdominal scoli; latter often profusely branched; anal plate smooth.
                                         HEMILEUCIDAE
  bb. Scoli alpha of mesothorax at least twice as long as scoli of abdominal segments 1 to 6; scoli never profusely branched; anal plate bearing at least one pair of small chitinous processes.   CERATOCAMPIDAE

Genera of Saturniidae:

a. Eighth abdominal segment bearing a scolus on the dorsomeson.
  b. Scoli alpha of mesothorax and metathorax subequal in size to or smaller than other body scoli; scolus Pi never present on abdominal segments 1 and 2.
    c. Scoli well developed and conspicuous, cylindrical, higher than wide.   *Philosamia*
    cc. Scoli reduced to small knobs not higher than wide.
      d. Labrum notched to about one-half its depth; secondary setae rare or absent on dorsum.   *Rothschildia*
      dd. Labrum notched to three-fourths its depth; secondary setae common on dorsum.
        e. Abdominal segments 1 to 7 each bearing a transverse yellow intersegmental stripe; scoli Rho and Kappa not connected by a yellowish ridge; spiracle much closer to scolus Kappa than to Rho.   *Tropea*

ee. Abdominal segments not bearing intersegmental stripes but scoli Rho and Kappa connected by a yellowish ridge; spiracle about half way between scoli Rho and Kappa.

Telea

bb. Scoli alpha of mesothorax and metathorax larger than those of abdominal segments 2 to 6.

c. Abdominal segments 1 and 2 bearing two scoli below spiracle; scoli alpha of first abdominal segment much larger than those of second.

Samia

cc. Abdominal segments 1 and 2 bearing one scolus or none below spiracle, or sometimes a second one, very rudimentary; scoli alpha of first abdominal segment not much larger than those of second.

Callosamia

aa. Eighth abdominal segment not bearing a scolus on the dorsomeson.

b. Secondary setae numerous and long, obscuring the scoli, which are reduced.

Agapema

bb. Secondary setae rare or absent; scoli conspicuous, subequal in size on all segments.

Saturnia

Genera of Hemileucidae:

a. Lateral spinules of supraspiracular scoli rho usually sparse, not obscuring axis of scolus; head smaller than prothorax; secondary setae often numerous; labrum shallowly notched.

b. Scoli alpha of abdomen modified into verricules strikingly different from other scoli.

c. Body covered with small white dots, each dot surrounding the base of a secondary seta; colors variegated.   *Hemileuca*

cc. Body not covered with white dots, unicolorous (except in *P. hera).*

Pseudohazis

bb. Scoli alpha of abdomen similar to those of other parts of the body.

Coloradia

aa. Lateral spinules of supraspiracular scoli Rho long, thickly set, obscuring axis of scolus; head larger than prothorax; secondary setae of body rare; labrum notched to more than one-half its depth.

Automeris

Genera of Ceratocampidae:

a. Secondary setae numerous, conspicuous, and distinctly longer than scoli of abdomen.

Basilona

aa. Secondary setae above level of prolegs inconspicuous.

b. Eighth abdominal segment bearing a scolus on the dorsomeson (Fig. 110); armature of metathorax similar to that of mesothorax.

c. Prothorax bearing well developed scoli; abdominal scoli slender, echinulate.

Citheronia

cc. Prothorax bearing rudimentary scoli; abdominal scoli broad at
    base, pointed, smooth.
    d. Scoli of abdominal segments 1, 3, and 5 one fourth as long as
       those of 2, 4, and 6; those of segment 9 abortive.
                                                  Adelocephala
    dd. Scoli of abdominal segments 1 to 6 uniform in size; those of
       segment 9 conspicuous.   *Syssphinx*
  bb. Eighth abdominal segment without a scolus on the dorsomeson
    (Fig. 111).   *Anisota*

    Philosamia cynthia is the only American species of its genus. The
caterpillars have a creamy appearance owing to a powdery bloom which
somewhat obscures the blue scoli.
    Rothschildia jorulla was studied but *R. orizaba* has not been seen.
    Tropea luna, when the caterpillar is fully grown, is of a clear
green color on both its head and body. On the caudal margin of each abdominal segment there is a transverse yellow line and another on either
side of the body below the spiracles. The scoli are reddish in color
and rather small in size.
    Telea polyphemus is very similar to *Tropea luna* except in the
characters given in the key.
    Samia cecropia was the only one of the North American species of
this genus examined. The enlarged dorsal scoli of the mesothorax, metathorax, and first abdominal segment distinguish this species from all
other members of the family.
    Callosamia. Two species of this genus occur in the eastern states
and one (*C. calleta*) in the southwest, Mexico and Arizona. They may
be distinguished as follows:

a. Scoli of first eight abdominal segments reduced or absent in last
   larval instars.
  b. Abdomen bearing a distinct longitudinal subspiracular yellow
    ridge.   *C. angulifera*
  bb. Abdomen not bearing a subspiracular ridge.   *C. promethea*
aa. Scoli of first eight abdominal segments conspicuous, those of first
   segment largest; body marked with black, base of scoli red.
                                      C. calleta

    Agapema anona is a conspicuously marked yellow and black species
with a black head. *A. galbina* has not been seen.

    The three species of Saturnia examined (*pavonia-major, pavonia-
minor,* and *spini*) are all exotic. The larva of *S. mendocino* seems not
to be known at the present time.
    Hemileuca. In both this genus and Pseudohazis the scoli alpha of

the last two thoracic and first eight abdominal segments are modified
into verricules or thick bunches of short stiff setae. Other scoli are
normal. Three species *(grotei, juno,* and *tricolor)* have not been seen.
Pseudohazis hera is included in the following synopsis of the species of
Hemileuca because the writer was unable to distinguish between specimens of the larvae labeled with this name in the United States National
Museum and those of *H. electra.*

a. Verricules alpha of mesothorax each surrounding a scolus which
    arises from its center and makes the verricule conspicuously differ-
    ent from those of the metathorax.
   b. Secondary setae numerous, about half as long as scoli and often
     as long as verricules.   *H. neumoegenii*
  bb. Secondary setae when present sparse and short.
   c. Dorsal abdominal verricules yellow or light brown, always lighter
     in color than the scoli.
    d. Body with pale areas conspicuous, more extensive than dark
      areas.   *H. nevadensis*
    dd. Body very dark, pale areas confined to minute dots.
                                         H. maia var. *lucina*
   cc. Dorsal abdominal verricules as dark in color as the scoli, usually
     dark brown or black, at least at tip.   *H. maia*
aa. Verricules of mesothorax similar to those of metathorax, not sur-
    rounding scoli.
   b. Secondary setae numerous, subequal to dorsal verricules in length.
                                            H. electra
                                 Pseudohazis hera
  bb. Secondary setae sparse, much shorter than verricules.
                              H. hualapai var. *oliviae*

    Pseudohazis. Whatever the family arrangement in Saturnioidea,
Pseudohazis and *Hemileuca* must be placed together for they are very
similar. The difference given in the synopsis is not a good one (altho
it seems to hold for all species except *Pseudohazis hera* of the north
Pacific states) but I am unable to improve on it at present. *P. hera*
may be separated from the other species by the numerous white dots at
the bases of the secondary setae and is thus a typical Hemileuca. In
P. eglanterina most of the setae are light in color but the body and
verricules are a dead black. The verricules of *P. shastaensis* are light
in color at base and tipped with black, the body color varying in different
individuals.
    Automeris. The caterpillar of the Io moth *(A. io)* is well known
and its poisonous spines are rather notorious. The variety *fuscus* Lu-
ther, also found in the Eastern states, has the scoli much smaller, leav-

ing a great part of each segment unprotected. In *io* the entire body surface seems to be covered.

Coloradia pandora was seen only in the early larval stages, when the scoli are long and sparsely branched. These may possibly become reduced in the mature larva. Between and slightly behind scoli Rho and alpha on the abdomen is a single seta, beta.

Basilona imperialis. The larva of the yellow imperial moth is well known; the long setae enable it to be identified at a glance.

Citheronia. The caterpillar of *C. regalis* is commonly known as the "Hickory Horned Devil", the horns being the subdorsal scoli of the meso- and metathorax. In this species each of these segments is armed with a pair of very long scoli on each side while in *C. sepulchralis* but one long scolus is found on each side on each of the two segments; in other words the former species has scoli Rho very well developed on the thorax, while in the latter scolus Rho is no larger than Kappa or Pi.

Adelocephala. The one species of this genus, *A. bicolor,* is very similar to Syssphinx in the larval stage, but the reduced armature on each alternate abdominal segment and the echinulate mesothoracic scoli serve to separate them.

Syssphinx. Peculiar smooth processes, similar to the thorns of a rose, take the place of scoli in *S. heiligbrodti,* the only species I have examined, and make it recognizable at a glance. Even the thoracic scoli are nearly smooth. As the genus is distinct from other Saturnians in adult characters, it is probable that these processes occur in the other two American species, *S. bisecta* and *S. quadrilineata.*

Anisota. While the species of *Anisota* are very common, their small size and plain appearance have caused them to attract less attention than their relatives. They may be easily distinguished from each other as follows:

a. Scoli alpha of abdominal segments 1 to 6 very much reduced and inconspicuous; scoli Kappa well developed; caudal projections of suranal plate scarcely longer than lateral processes.   *A. rubicunda*
aa. Scoli alpha of abdominal segments 1 to 6 subequal to Kappa in size.
  b. Scoli alpha of abdominal segments 1 to 6 much shorter than thoracic legs.
    c. Caudal projections of suranal plate distinctly longer than wide, pointing directly caudad; body with conspicuous black longitudinal stripes, not dotted.   *A. senatoria*
    cc. Caudal projections of suranal plate about as long as base is wide, pointing caudodorsad; body without black stripes but covered with minute dots.   *A. virginiensis*

bb. Scoli alpha of abdominal segments 1 to 6 conspicuous, about as long as thoracic legs.

c. Body uniformly and closely tuberculate, stripes faint.

A. stigma

cc. Body irregularly and rather sparsely tuberculate; stripes conspicuous.

A. consularis

Thauma and *Hylesia*. No specimens of these genera were available for study.

SUPERFAMILY SPHINGOIDEA

The Sphingidae, the only members of this superfamily, include some of our largest caterpillars. The variation in structure, while not great, is, according to Forbes (1911) sufficient to enable the different genera to be easily identified. His synopsis of the genera and discussion of the species are of great value to anyone with larvae to determine. The family characters are as follows:

Head usually smaller than prothorax, usually partially retractile, shorter in dorsal than in ventral portion, always more or less narrowed above; head in Lapara high and conical above, much higher, tho no wider, than body; setae of head minute and numerous, present on all parts except labrum and mouth parts; front reaching less than half the distance to vertical triangle; labrum variously notched. Body cylindrical, plump; secondary setae present on prolegs but rare or absent on body; primary setae reduced or wanting; when present, kappa and eta distant, eta farther dorsad than kappa and almost as high as spiracle; segment 8 bearing a slender horn in most genera; when reduced, a scar or corniculum marks its location except in Lapara. Prolegs present and large, set close together, bearing biordinal crochets arranged in a mesoseries. Anal prolegs flattened laterad, forming, with the suranal plate, a triangular pyramid.

RHOPALOCERA

The butterflies seem to have been separated from other Lepidoptera at a very remote period. They have been specialized in all stages along entirely different lines. The larvae seem to have separated from the Microlepidoptera before the time when kappa and eta became adjacent on the abdomen.

Scudder's "Butterflies of the Eastern United States and Canada" is at present *the* authority on all stages of Rhopalocera. So many entomologists have no access to a copy of this beautiful but expensive work, however, that it is considered worth while to cover the group so far as possible here. Many of the characters are adapted from his descriptions and a free use has been made of his method of separating the genera.

On the basis of larval structure the butterflies may be divided into about five groups. In the Hesperioidea, including the Hesperiidae and Megathymidae, the crochets are triordinal and arranged in a complete circle, and the body bears very short numerous secondary setae but no other form of armature. The larvae of the Lycaenoidea (the Lycaenidae and Riodinidae) are somewhat onisciform in shape, the head small and retractile, the body covered with coarse secondary setae. Forbes has called attention to the peculiar form of the prolegs, which bear an interrupted mesoseries of crochets with a spatulate fleshy lobe arising near the interruption. The Papilionidae and Parnassiidae are characterized by the presence of prothoracic osmateria; in the former the body is practically without setae, but both secondary setae and verrucae are present in the latter. The Pieridae are considered by many as belonging to the Papilionoidea but the larvae are not closely related. All the remaining families, Libytheidae, Lymnadidae, Ithomiidae, Heliconiidae, Agapetidae, and Nymphalidae, may be grouped together as Nymphaloidea, altho they have few larval structures in common. They are all armed with scoli or fleshy filaments or a bifurcate suranal plate, except the Libytheidae, which are distinguished from the others by the pseudocircular arrangement of the crochets.

FAMILY HESPERIIDAE

The conspicuous structure of the larvae of skippers is the large head attached to a strongly constricted "collar". This head is covered with numerous secondary setae, often plumose but never long, sometimes borne on chalazae. The labrum is shallowly concave at tip and usually a shallow mesal groove is present on the cephalic surface. The front extends about two-thirds of the distance to the top of the head.

The body is either cylindrical or fusiform, widest at the proleg-bearing segments, usually tapering considerably toward each end; secondary setae numerous, often very short; small flattened plates sometimes present, possibly showing position of primary setae; segments divided into indistinct annulets, incisions all shallow or obscure; prothoracic shield narrow, often indistinct. Prolegs with triordinal crochets in a complete circle.

Scudder divides the family into Hesperidi and Pamphilidi and gives a table for the separation of the genera of the former group in all stages. The family is so poorly represented at the National Museum that at present nothing can be added to his work.

FAMILY MEGATHYMIDAE

No species of this small family is found east of the Rocky Mountains and even there the boring habit of the larvae makes their discovery difficult. Three specimens of *Megathymus yuccae* have been examined and the following characters are taken from them.

Head rounded, about as high as wide, rugose, partially retractile, smaller than prothorax; front triangular, sides almost straight, reaching about half way to top of head; labrum with a small, acute, mesal notch; setae very much reduced; ocelli small, inconspicuous. Prothoracic shield narrow, sometimes indistinct; setae of body much reduced, apparently wanting on its dorsal half, numerous and short on ventral half of first two thoracic segments, rare or absent on abdomen, except on prolegs. Thoracic legs well developed, bearing numerous setae on their caudomesal surfaces; prolegs short, bearing a complete ellipse of biordinal crochets, series sometimes slightly broken at mesal and lateral ends; spiracles large, those of segment 8 placed somewhat farther dorsad than the others.

FAMILY LYCAENIDAE

Head from one-sixth to one-half as wide as body, usually deeply retractile, often overhung by the prothorax; front broad, often extending over half way to vertical triangle; labrum various. Body depressed, widest above prolegs, usually tapering strongly toward the ends; secondary setae numerous, sometimes in tufts and pencils, usually coarse and short. This form of body does not occur elsewhere in Lepidoptera except in the Zygaenoidea. Prolegs with a mesoseries of triordinal crochets well developed at the ends of the series, shorter or interrupted at the middle, and with a spatulate or clavate fleshy lobe arising near the interruption (Fig. 79).

From the very meager material at hand, the following synopsis has been prepared. It follows to some extent that of Scudder:

a. Head at least one-third the diameter of the body.
  b. Head about one-half the diameter of the body.
    c. Verrucae large and distinct, with short setae.   *Eumaeus*
    cc. Verrucae inconspicuous or absent, setae long, arranged in transverse groups.
                                                        Feniseca
  bb. Head about one-third the diameter of the body.
    c. Lateral line continuous and rather conspicuous.
      d. Prothorax longer and higher than mesothorax; abdomen marked by a pair of subdorsal lines between mediodorsal and lateral lines.   *Mitoura*

dd. Prothorax much smaller than mesothorax; abdomen usually not marked by subdorsal lines. *Thecla*
cc. Lateral line discontinuous and faint or absent.
  d. Labrum notched to about one-third its depth. *Chrysophanus*
  dd. Labrum very shallowly concave at tip.
    e. Body widest in metathoracic region, tapering rapidly cephalad and gradually caudad.
      f. Fifth ocellus located below center of arc formed by first four ocelli; second ocellus out of line, making arc uneven. *Calycopys*
      ff. Fifth ocellus located at center of arc formed by first four ocelli; arc regular, even. *Heodes*
    ee. Body widest in region of segment 6 of abdomen, tapering gradually cephalad and rapidly caudad. *Uranotes*
aa. Head less than one-fourth the diameter of the body.
  b. Body marked by longer setae on outer margin of narrow dorsal area than on other parts.
    c. Anal segment broad and greatly depressed. *Everes*
Philotes
    cc. Anal segment narrow and moderately depressed. *Cyaniris*
  bb. Body covered with setae of uniform length throughout.
    c. Setae of body long, closely set; vertical triangle rather broad. *Nomiades*
    cc. Setae of body short, rather sparse; vertical triangle very narrow. *Rusticus*

This synopsis was prepared to cover the following species. All were examined in the National Museum except those marked with an asterisk and they are carefully described by Scudder:

Eumaeus atala   *Chrysophanus thoe*
Feniseca tarquinius   *Calycopys cecrops*
Mitoura damon   *Heodes hypophleas*
Thecla adenostomatis   *Uranotes melinus*
  T. edwardsii   *Everes comyntas*
  T. liparops   *Philotes sonorensis*
  T. calanus   *Cyaniris ladon (pseudargiolus)*
  T. acadica   *Nomiades couperii**
  T. spini of Europe   *Rusticus melissa*
                                    *R. scudderii**

Family Riodinidae

No riodinid larvae have been seen. The group is sometimes called a subfamily of Lycaenidae to which it is closely related. The head is said to be about half the diameter of the subonisciform body. In the

absence of material it is impossible to be sure that the prolegs and crochets are of the peculiar form seen in Lycaenidae.

FAMILY LIBYTHEIDAE

American larvae of this family are not known to me, but the following characters, for which Edwards is the authority, are duplicated in
Libythea celtis of Europe.

Hypatus bachmani. Body cylindrical, somewhat thickened in region of last two thoracic segments; dorsum of last two abdominal segments curved abruptly ventrad; each segment divided into four or five
annulets; numerous secondary setae present, a group at the base of each
leg and one on the first annulet of each segment, borne on chalazae.

In addition, *L. celtis* has the head covered with secondary setae,
the second, third, and fourth ocelli on papillae, the other ocelli reduced,
and the crochets arranged in a pseudocircle. The labrum is shallowly
concave at tip. The general structure and habits are similar to those
of the Pieridae, but the presence of the lateral rudimentary crochets of
the pseudocircle will distinguish them.

The larva of *Hypatus carinenta* seems to be unknown.

FAMILY LYMNADIDAE

Head about as large as prothorax, bilobed; labrum with a rounded
emargination. Body bearing fleshy filaments in the subdorsal region
(Fig. 92), at least on the mesothorax; not more than three pairs of these
processes present in American species; coloration always consisting of
transverse black and green stripes.

Anosia plexippus bears a pair of these filaments on the mesothorax
and another pair on the eighth abdominal segment. There are three
transverse black stripes on each segment. *A. berenice* bears filaments
on the mesothorax and the second and eighth abdominal segments. The
middle of each segment bears a wide double broken black band reaching
over the dorsum to the end of each proleg.

Lycorea cleobaea is the only species of Lycorea north of Mexico.
No specimens of the larvae are in the National Museum; but a related
species, *L. atergatis* of southern Mexico, has fleshy filaments on the
mesothorax only, and the black color on the abdomen covers the venter
and the intersegmental incisions.

FAMILY ITHOMIIDAE

The larvae of the three North American species of these Nymphaloidea seem to be unknown. Wilhelm Müller (1886) describes in a brief
way other species of the same genera but gives no very definite structural data. The only distinguishing characters mentioned are arrange-

ments of the setae in the first larval instar. In later stages numerous secondary setae are present and sometimes small cornicula ("zipfel") below the spiracle, but no other form of armature.

FAMILY HELICONIIDAE

But one species of this large tropical group ranges into the United States. The larvae are all typical Nymphalidae in most particulars. The characters given are drawn from *Apostraphia charithonia* of Florida but they apply also to most of the known South American forms.

Head distinctly bilobed, bearing a long, slender scolus on each lobe; front not reaching half way to top of head; color green with ocelli located on a black spot and another pair of black spots on the epicranium near the union of the arms of the epicranial suture.

Prothorax smaller than head, bearing a dorsal shield; shield with one large seta but no scoli; mesothorax and metathorax each bearing a subdorsal pair of scoli and one on each side slightly above the spiracular level; no subspiracular scoli present on thorax, but several verrucae located at the base of each leg. Abdomen with three scoli present on each side on each segment, one subdorsal, one supraspiracular, and one subspiracular; no scoli on dorsomeson; small chalaza or scolus present on abdominal segments 1, 2, 7, and 8, in line with prolegs in the position of the Pi group and another very small one in the position of sigma; scoli all very long and slender, nearly as long as body is wide; secondary setae minute or absent above level of prolegs, small on ventral surface. Prolegs all present and well developed; crochets biordinal or triordinal, arranged in a mesoseries.

The above description applies equally well in almost every particular to Agraulis of the Nymphalidae, but in that genus the scoli are not quite so long and slender. The shape of the head offers the most convenient means of differentiating the two genera, altho the difference is hard to describe. In the Heliconiidae the head scoli are located back of the plane of the front and are not borne on conical projections of the head. The scoli of Agraulis are borne on prominent conical projections which gradually merge into the scoli and which extend cephalodorsad so that the bases of the scoli are somewhat cephalad of the plane of the front.

FAMILY AGAPETIDAE

The larvae of the satyrs differ from other Nymphaloidea in several particulars and their external characters do not indicate a very close relationship. All their relatives except Anaea and Hypatus have an external armature consisting of scoli or fleshy filaments. On the other hand none but the Agapetidae have a bifurcate suranal plate.

Head as large as, or larger than, prothorax, which usually forms a constricted neck; surface rugose or tuberculated; shape varying from rounded above to bilobed or horned; labrum usually deeply emarginate; ocelli in most or all species with the third ocellus borne on an elevated tubercle and very much larger than the others. Body with numerous, well developed, lenticle-like papillae bearing small secondary setae; segments divided into annulets usually six in number; suranal plate bifurcate, bearing a pair of very rugose conical projections (Fig. 84). Prolegs bearing a mesoseries of uniordinal, biordinal, or triordinal crochets.

Genera of Agapetidae:

a. Head rounded above, not bearing conspicuous scoli, not with laterodorsal angles.

   b. Caudal processes widely separated, as far apart as long, parallel (Fig. 84).   *Cercyonis*

   bb. Caudal processes almost contiguous at base, divergent.

     c. Mediodorsal and lateral stripes conspicuous.   *Oeneis*

     cc. Mediodorsal and lateral stripes indistinct.   *Coenonympha*

aa. Head bearing a pair of conspicuous dorsal prominences, sometimes reduced to sharp laterodorsal angles.

   b. Dorsal prominence about as long as head is wide.

     c. Head, including prominences, about once and a half as high as wide.   *Enodia*

     cc. Head, including prominences, about twice as high as wide.

                                        Satyrodes

   bb. Dorsal prominences reduced to low knobs.

     c. Larger papillae of head few and sparse.   *Neonympha*

     cc. Larger papillae of head closely placed.   *Cissia*

The discussion and key are based on the following species; those not seen by the writer but described by Scudder are marked with an asterisk (*):

*Cercyonis meadii, C. alope**
Oeneis chryxus, O. jutta, O. norna*
Coenonympha typhon, C. elko
Enodia portlandia
*Satyrodes canthus**
*Neonympha phocion**
Cissia eurytus, C. sosybius**

Family Nymphalidae

Even when limited by the removal of the other Nymphaloidea, this family is a large and varied group. Scudder divides it into five tribes which are distinct in all stages; and these tribes are retained here as subfamilies.   All of these species possess scoli, either on the head or body, except some of the Apaturinae, especially Anaea. This distinguishes them from all other butterfly larvae.

The separation from the Saturnioidea is more difficult.   The arrangement of the scoli is apparently the same in the two families but is modified in different ways.   In no nymphalids are mediodorsal scoli limited to segments 8 and 9 when they are present at all. The genera in which they are absent from the dorsomeson and in which the head scoli are also absent are Euptoieta, Speyeria and Anaea.   The first is made conspicuous by the great development of the subdorsal scoli on the prothorax, and the last by the very large head; but no way of separating the species of Speyeria from those of Saturnia is known to me. Unfortunately no specimens of Speyeria have been available and I am compelled to rely upon Edwards' description. It is probable that the head of the saturnian is much smaller, that the crochets are more regularly biordinal, and that the anal prolegs are much larger than in Speyeria.

The work of Wilhelm Müller (1886) on this family is a classic. It is particularly notable as being the earliest scientific study of all the stages of the larvae of any group. His demonstration of the fact that the scoli have no relation to the primary setae is conclusive and is the reason for the omission here of the nomenclature used in other parts of the paper. Instead, terms are used denoting position, especially the following: mediodorsal, subdorsal, supraspiracular, subspiracular, and subventral. Their meaning is obvious and they answer as well as symbols in cases where there is but one transverse row of scoli, or other form of armature, to the segment, as in this group.

Subfamilies of Nymphalidae:

a. Scoli always present, usually subequal in size, never five times as long on mesothorax as on abdominal segments 1, 3, 5, and 6.
   b. Mediodorsal scoli never present on abdominal segments; head rarely bearing numerous secondary setae.   ARGYNNINAE
  bb. Mediodorsal scoli present on at least a few abdominal segments; head usually bearing numerous secondary setae.
    c. Abdomen bearing a pair of scoli at base of each proleg similar to dorsal scoli in shape, but smaller; lateral setae of all scoli slender, closely placed; two mediodorsal scoli on segment 8 or one each on segments 8 and 9.   MELITAEINAE
   cc. Abdomen bearing a single scolus or none at the base of each proleg; when present, shorter than other scoli; lateral setae of dorsal scoli stout, sparse (Fig. 74); only one mediodorsal scolus on segment 8, none on segment 9 (Fig. 112).   VANESSINAE

aa. Scoli often wanting, when present ten times as long on mesothorax
  as on abdominal segments 1, 3, 5 or 6.
  b. Mesothorax bearing scoli about as long as body is wide.
                                                                    NYMPHALINAE
  bb. Mesothorax without scoli.   APATURINAE
  Genera of Argynninae:

a. Abdominal scoli over half as long as segments.
  b. Subdorsal prothoracic scoli twice as long as those of abdomen,
    clavate; head bigibbous, rounded.   *Euptoieta*
  bb. Subdorsal prothoracic scoli smaller than those of abdomen, not
    clavate.
    c. Head armed above with long scoli or short, pointed prominences;
      abdominal scoli not longer than those of thorax.
      d. Scoli of head long, spine-like; subdorsal pair of prothorax
        rudimentary.   *Agraulis*
      dd. Scoli of head short, not spine-like; subdorsal pair of protho-
        rax about as long as those of abdomen.   *Argynnis*
    cc. Head rounded above, bigibbous, not armed with scoli or pointed
      prominences; abdominal scoli longer than those of thorax.
                                                            Speyeria
aa. Abdominal scoli less than half as long as segments; head rounded,
  bigibbous; prothoracic scoli sometimes long.   *Brenthis*
  Genera of Melitaeinae:

a. Subspiracular scoli present on all three thoracic segments.
  b. Mediodorsal scoli light in color, others black; body with numerous
    slender secondary setae.   *Lemonias*
  bb. Mediodorsal scoli black, like the others; body with stout, sparse
    secondary setae.   *Euphydryas*
aa. Subspiracular scolus present on mesothorax but absent or reduced
  to a single seta on metathorax.
  b. Dorsal scoli stout, sometimes verruca-like, about twice as high as
    broad.   *Phyciodes*
  bb. Dorsal scoli slender, at least three times as high as broad.
    c. Dorsal abdominal scoli not as long as segments, subequal in
      length to those of metathorax.
      d. Dorsal scoli of mesothorax and metathorax subequal in size;
        body striped, not spotted.
        e. Supraspiracular scolus of segment 8 dorsad and only
          slightly cephalad of spiracle; body with conspicuous trans-
          verse stripes.   *Cinclidia*
        ee. Supraspiracular scolus of segment 8 cephalad of top of

spiracle, much farther cephalad than subspiracular; stripes longitudinal.	*Charidryas*

dd. Dorsal scoli of mesothorax at least one and a half times as long as those of metathorax; body closely spotted; each segment bearing a large red dorsal macula.	*Chlosyne*

cc. Dorsal abdominal scoli much shorter than those of mesothorax and metathorax; supraspiracular scolus of abdominal segment 8 dorsad of spiracle; stripes longitudinal.	*Thessalia*

Genera of Vanessinae:

a. Head bearing a pair of dorsal scoli.

　b. Spinules of body scoli erect; subapical ones in a whorl (Fig. 74).

　　c. Mediodorsal scoli present on all abdominal segments; head scoli no higher than head is wide.	*Polygonia*

　　cc. Mediodorsal scoli present only on abdominal segments 7 and 8; head scoli twice as high as head is wide.	*Mestra*

　bb. Spinules of body scoli appressed, not arranged in a whorl; head scoli not clavate.

　　c. Dorsal scoli of head low, strongly tapering, concolorous with head, indefinite at base; body scoli needle-like, with two or three principal spinules.	*Eugonia*

　　cc. Dorsal scoli of head cylindrical, distinct at base, darker than dorsal part of head; body scoli cylindrical, rather stout, with numerous lateral spinules.	*Junonia*

aa. Head rounded above, bigibbous, bearing chalazae but no scoli.

　b. Mediodorsal scolus absent on abdominal segments 1 and 2, present on segments 4 to 8, usually also on segment 3.	*Euvanessa*

　bb. Mediodorsal scoli present on abdominal segment 2.

　　c. Mediodorsal scoli present on segments 1 to 8 inclusive.

Vanessa
Aglais

　　cc. Mediodorsal scolus absent from segment 1.

Genera of Nymphalinae:

a. Abdominal segments 3 and 8 bearing scoli as long as those of mesothorax.	*Limenitis*

aa. Abdominal segments 3 and 8 without scoli or with small ones.

Basilarchia

Genera of Apaturinae:

a. Head crowned by a pair of scoli; suranal plate bifurcate.	*Chlorippe*

aa. Head crowned only by a few low tubercles; suranal plate entire.

Anaea

The following species of the Nymphalidae have been examined by the writer and on them the preceding synopsis is based.

Argynninae
    Euptoieta claudia
    Agraulis vanillae
    Argynnis cybele
Melitaeinae
    Lemonias chalcedon
        L. macglashani
        L. baroni
        L. editha
    Euphydryas phaeton
    Phyciodes montana
    Cinclidia harrisii
    Charidryas nycteis
        C. ismeria
    Chlosyne lacinia
    Thessalia leanira
Vanessinae
    Polygonia interrogationis
        P. satyrus
        P. zephyrus
        P. comma

Vanessinae (continued)
    Mestra amymone
    Eugonia californica
    Junonia coenia
    Euvanessa antiopa
    Vanessa atalanta
        V. huntera
        V. cardui
        V. caryae
    Aglais milberti
Nymphalinae
    Limenitis bredowii var. *californica*
    Basilarchia archippus
        B. astyanax
Apaturinae
    Chlorippe clyton
        C. alicia
        C. celtis
    Anaea andria

Scudder has described and figured the following in addition to some of the above and their place in the synopsis is based on his descriptions.

Argynninae
    Argynnis aphrodite
        A. atlantis
    Speyeria idalia
    Brenthis myrina
        B. montinus
        B. bellona

FAMILY PIERIDAE

Altho closely related to Papilionidae, the larvae of Pieridae are of a generalized structure little resembling their more advanced relatives. They seem to be characterized principally by a *lack* of osmateria, fleshy filaments, cephalic or anal horns, or special developments of the prolegs. Chalazae, the only form of armature present, make some of the secondary setae much more conspicuous than others. The conspicuous setae are not the "primary" ones, as Forbes seems to have assumed; they are too numerous and not in the right locations.

Head about as large as prothorax, not retractile except in *Phoebis*, distinct from prothorax and with caudal half well developed; front extending about half way to top of head; labrum moderately emarginate; numerous secondary setae present, varying from minute to large and borne on papillae of various sizes; surface of head varying from nearly smooth to rugose and irregular. Body bearing numerous secondary setae, sometimes all similar, usually of widely different sizes and borne on chalazae varying from microscopic to conspicuous; segments divided into annulets, usually six in number, each annulet bearing either a single row of setae or a band nearly its full width. Prolegs present on segments 3, 4, 5, 6, and 10, all similar in size; crochets biordinal or triordinal, always arranged in a mesoseries.

The following synopsis includes six of the nine genera occurring north of Florida and east of Texas and the Rocky Mountains. No specimens of *Nathalis iole*, *Zerene caesonia*, or *Pyrisita mexicana* of the southern states have been available. Larvae of all of the northern species east of the Rockies have been examined except *Eurymus interior*.

Genera of Pieridae:

a. Setae of head borne on chalazae, those of front much smaller than those laterad of the epicranial suture.
  b. Head with many chalazae as high as tubercles on which ocelli are placed, about as conspicuous as those of thorax.
    c. Prothoracic legs at least half as long as mesothoracic.   *Pontia*
    cc. Prothoracic legs much less than half as long as mesothoracic.
                                    Callidryas

  bb. Head with chalazae usually lower than ocellar tubercles; when a few are well developed they are not one-fourth as large as those of prothorax.   *Synchloe*
aa. Setae of head usually not borne on chalazae, those of front always similar to those laterad of the epicranial suture; setae of body all minute and similar.
  b. Head about one-third as wide as abdomen, deeply retractile.
                                      Phoebis

  bb. Head at least half as wide as abdomen, scarcely retractile.
    c. Body setae not on chalazae or on very small ones.   *Eurymus*
    cc. Body setae borne on distinct chalazae, higher than wide.
                                     Eurema

Pontia monuste and *Pontia protodice* have many of the chalazae much larger than others, while *P. rapae* and *P. napi* (including var. *oleracea*) usually have all the chalazae small and subequal in size.

Neither of the two species of Callidryas have been available but the genus was placed in the table on the authority of Scudder's detailed description of *C. eubule*.

Synchloe (=Anthocharis) has several and various forms of larvae. In *S. genutia* some of the prothoracic chalazae are very large and those of the head are well developed, while in *S. sara* and *S. olympia* the setae of the head and prothorax are all small and borne on small chalazae.

The larva of *Phoebis argante* var. *maxima* Neum. is large with a small retractile head.

The bright green larva of *Eurymus philodice* is well known in the eastern half of the United States. It has a pair of distinct lateral lines and a black spot below the line on each segment. *E. eurytheme* which ranges eastward to some extent from its home in the Rocky Mountains has a similar larval stage except that the black spots are either indistinct or connected from one segment to another.

Eurema nicippe has the setae all about the same size. The larger chalazae of the head are larger than the ocelli. The larva of *E. euterpe* (=*lisa*) is less than three-fourths of an inch long and the chalazae of the head are all small.

FAMILY PAPILIONIDAE

Larvae of the Swallow-tail butterflies are, like the adults, beautifully decorated and outlined. No unpleasant spines or horns are present to discourage the observer and no discordant colors to offend him. The structure of all the species is so constant that it is necessary to have recourse to color in their separation, but all of the characters used are fixed and are seldom affected by alcoholic or other means of preservation.

Head smaller than prothorax, somewhat retractile, shorter in dorsal than in ventral portion; front not extending half way to top of head; labrum notched to about half its depth and bearing about thirty setae; ocelli six, subequal in size, fifth much closer to fourth than to sixth; secondary setae short. Body cylindrical, usually tapering rather abruptly toward the head and gradually toward the caudal end, usually widest in the region of the first abdominal segment; setae reduced or absent on body but numerous on prolegs; intersegmental incisions inconspicuous; prolegs short, bearing a mesoseries of triordinal crochets, sometimes with a lateral row, forming a pseudocircle; lateral crochets, when present, smaller than mesal, and biordinal. Osmaterium always present; when retracted its location is shown by a long transverse groove on the dorsum of the prothorax. In alcoholic specimens inserting the points of a small pair of forceps assures the observer of the nature of this groove and does no damage.

Scudder divides the family into six genera, each including but one or two species found in New England. Dyar's List discards three of

them, uniting them under the name Papilio, but retains Laertias and
Iphiclides. A study of the larvae of ten species of Dyar's Papilio,
twice as many as Scudder had, shows the justification of Scudder's
view, four distinct forms of larvae being found. As it would be very
inconvenient to tabulate species of the family when using Papilio in the
broader sense, the writer has returned to Scudder's arrangement. It
might also be mentioned that the structure of the pupae upholds his
position.

Genera of Papilionidae:

a. Body bearing several rows of fleshy filaments or filamentous processes.
Laertias

aa. Body without processes of any kind, except osmateria.
  b. Crochets arranged in a pseudocircle; metathorax bearing an eye-
    spot.
    c. Prothorax bearing a small transverse black shield; lateral line
      conspicuous; first abdominal segment bearing two black spots
      near its caudal margin but no continuous transverse black
      band. *Euphoeades*
    cc. Prothoracic shield indistinct, not black; lateral line inconspicu-
      ous; first abdominal segment bearing a continuous transverse
      black or yellow band near its caudal margin. *Jasoniades*
  bb. Crochets not arranged in a pseudocircle, no lateral crochets being
    present; metathorax not bearing an eyespot.
    c. Coloration not segmentally arranged; metathorax with a slight
      transverse dorsal swelling. *Heraclides*
    cc. Coloration segmentally arranged; metathorax without a dorsal
      swelling.
      d. Each abdominal segment bearing a transverse black band
        marked with or interrupted by circular yellow spots and
        usually bordered by two transverse green stripes; narrower
        black transverse intersegmental stripe also present in each
        incision. *Papilio*
      dd. Each abdominal segment bearing a series of five transverse
        black stripes. *Iphiclides*

Laertias philenor is distinguished from all other insect larvae by
the possession of several pairs of fleshy filaments on each abdominal
segment.

Euphoeades troilus, in addition to the usual metathoracic eyespots,
has a distinct pair on the first abdominal segment; those of the metathorax are separated by a distance on the dorsum subequal to the width
of the outer circle of each eyespot. *E. palamedes* has an indistinct pair
on the first abdominal segment and the metathoracic pair are separated

by a distance three times as great as the width of the outer circle of each spot.

Jasoniades glaucus differs from other species of the genus Jasoniades in that the eyespot is single; that is, it is composed of a circle enclosing a smaller circle and a short rod, but is not associated with a smaller circle dorsad of the large one. The suture bounding the front is bluntly angulated at about the middle. In *J. daunus* the upper smaller figure of the double eyespot is rounded and the incisions between segments 5, 6, and 7 are marked with more or less distinct black lines. *J. eurymedon* and *J. rutulus* have the upper figure of the eyespot triangular and there are no black lines in the abdominal incisions, or else very faint ones. The former has the sides of the front arcuate while those of the latter are straight except for a very slight curve just where they unite.

Heraclides thoas (=cresphontes) is notable in having a conspicuous white mark covering segments 2, 3, and 4 and another on segments 7 and 8, while the rest of the body is a variegated reddish brown.

There remain for the genus Papilio the following species: *machaon, bairdii, zolicaon,* and *polyxenes,* all of which are very similar in coloration. At the same time there is such variation within species, especially as to the limits of these markings, that any suggestions as to their separation would be premature. *Papilio cresphontinus, americus,* and *indra* from the southern states and *P. brevicauda* from New England probably also belong here but they are so little known that their true position is somewhat uncertain.

Iphiclides ajax with its numerous transverse bands is quite distinct from all other members of the family.

Ithobalus. No specimens of the two species of this southern genus have been seen.

FAMILY PARNASSIIDAE

The parnassians seem to be an alpine or arctic group, for their American species are confined to the Rocky Mountains and Alaska. Their scarcity is to be regretted, for they retain many of the primitive characters of the Papilios. While the larvae have acquired osmateria, they still retain verrucae and conspicuous setae which are present only in the earlier larval stages of Papilionidae. As adults also, the venation is of the type found in Swallow-tails but the prolongations of the wings have not yet been developed. The following description is based on *Parnassius smintheus* of the Pacific States and it agrees in all important particulars with *P. apollo* of Europe. The only other species recorded south of Alaska is *P. clodius.*

Head rugose, black, about one-third the diameter of the abdomen, somewhat smaller than the prothorax; front small, wider than high, reaching about half way to top of head; labrum moderately emarginate, bearing only the six primary setae on each side; ocelli six, subequal in size, fifth much closer to fourth than to sixth; secondary setae of epicranium numerous but not long. Body cylindrical, scarcely tapering, covered with short, stout, secondary setae; thoracic segments with the verrucae of the Kappa and Pi groups, and sometimes those of Beta and Rho, distinct. Abdomen with Rho, kappa, eta, mu, and Pi forming distinct and separate verrucae; color black, except for several yellow subdorsal maculae on each segment; all setae black. Thoracic legs well developed, prolegs with a mesoseries of biordinal crochets extending more than half way round the planta; anal prolegs similar to ventral. Osmaterium present.

GLOSSARY

In the list of words on the following pages several new ones are included but most are words used here in a special sense. Smith's "Glossary of Entomology" and "The Standard dictionary" have proved most useful in its preparation altho no definitions from either are reproduced entire.

Adfrontal pieces, n. The narrow areas on the cephalic aspect of the head just laterad of the front. (Fig. 78.)

Anal prolegs, n. The prolegs of the last abdominal segment.

Anal segment, n. The tenth abdominal segment.

Annulet, n. One of the small rings into which a segment is divided by transverse constrictions.

Armature, n. The arrangement and form of all the setae and processes of the body wall.

Bigibbous, a. With a pair of large rounded dorsal swellings.

Biordinal, a. Said of crochets when they are arranged in a single series but are of at least two alternating lengths. (Fig. 106.)

Biserial, a. Said of crochets when they are arranged in two concentric rows. See multiserial.

Bisetose, a. Consisting of or bearing two setae; said of a group, such as Pi, or of a chalaza, pinaculum, etc.

Chaetotaxy, n. The arrangement of the setae of a particular insect or segment.

Chalaza, n. A small chitinized projection of cuticula bearing one seta or two to four setae on separate elevated prominences, between papillae and cornicula in size. (Fig. 90.)

Corniculum, n. A small horn-like process of cuticula, not associated with primary setae.

Coxa, n. The first segment of a thoracic leg.

Crochet, n. One of the series of chitinized, hook-like, cuticular structures usually arranged in rows or in a circle on the prolegs of lepidopterous larvae; also known as "hooks".

Epicranial suture, n. The suture separating the front from the rest of the epicranium, shaped like an inverted Y, with the front between the arms and the vertex on both sides of the stem. (Fig. 72.)

Epicranium, n. The sclerite which constitutes the greater part of the head capsule.

Fleshy filament, n. A flexible, attenuate process of the body wall, borne by some butterfly larvae. (Fig. 92.)

Front, n. The sclerite between the arms of the epicranial suture, usually triangular in shape.

Gibbous, a. With a large, rounded, dorsal hump.

Heteroideous, a. Said of crochets when a well developed series is flanked by a row of smaller crochets on each side, as in Arctiidae. (Fig. 100.)

Homoideous, a. Not heteroideous.

Homology, n. See Part One, p. 15.

Homotypy, n. See Part One, p. 15.

Horn, n. A stiff, pointed, unbranched, cuticular process.

Mesoseries, n. A band of crochets extending longitudinally on the mesal side of a proleg; when curved, varying from a quadrant to slightly more than a semicircle in extent. (Fig. 105.)

Moniliform, a. Possessing distinct, neck-like constrictions between successive segments, producing a resemblance to a string of beads, as in many leaf-miners.

Multiserial, a. Arranged in several concentric rows, as the crochets of Hepialus, Pseudanaphora, etc. (Figs. 94, 96.)

Multisetiferous, a. Bearing many setae.

Onisciform, a. Depressed and spindle-shaped, like an oniscid, as in some lycaenid larvae.

Osmaterium, n. An eversible gland producing an odor, as in Papilionidae and Liparidae.

Penellipse, n. A series of crochets more than a semicircle in extent and less than a complete circle. It may be either (a) lateral, covering at least the lateral half of the planta, as in Psychidae (Fig. 85); or (b) mesal, covering at least the mesal half of the proleg and interrupted laterally, as in Pyraustinae (Fig. 98).

Pinaculum, n. A small, flat, chitinized area bearing from one to four setae.

Plate, n. An extended chitinized area of the body wall, such as a shield; often multisetiferous.

Primary seta, n. A seta found on generalized larvae in all instars. When contrasted with "secondary setae" this term also applies to the few subprimary setae.

Proleg, n. A fleshy abdominal leg, said to be present when crochets are present even when there is no fleshy swelling.

Pseudocircle, n. An arrangement of crochets consisting of a well developed mesoseries and a row of small hooks on the lateral aspect of the proleg. (Fig. 97.)

Scolus, n. A spinose projection of the body wall, as in saturnian larvae. (Figs. 73, 74.)

Secondary setae, pl. n. Numerous setae having a general distribution and not limited to verrucae or other forms of tubercle. See page 23.

Seta, n. A chitinized, hair-like projection of cuticula arising from a single trichogen cell and surrounded at the base by a small cuticular ring.

Setiferous, a. Bearing one to many setae.

Shield, n. A chitinized plate covering the greater part of the dorsal half of a segment.

Sphingiform, a. Of the form of a sphingid caterpillar, having a cylindrical body, with setae very short or wanting and no other armature except a mediodorsal horn on the eighth abdominal segment.

Spinule, n. One of the short lateral branches of a scolus.

Stemapoda, pl. n. Elongated modifications of the anal prolegs in certain notodontid larvae.

Subprimary seta, n. A seta having a definite position in certain larvae but not present in the first instar of generalized groups. See Part One. For list of such setae, see pages 39, 40.

Suranal plate, n. A rather heavily chitinized area on the dorsum of the last abdominal segment. (Fig. 84.)

Triordinal, a. Said of crochets when they are of a single row but of three alternating lengths. (Fig. 98.)

Trisetose, a. Consisting of or bearing three setae; compare bisetose.

Tuft, n. A group of setae arising from a verruca.

Uniordinal, a. Said of crochets when they are arranged in a single row and are of a single length throughout or shorter toward the ends of the row; opposed to biordinal. (Figs. 101, 105.)

Uniserial, a. Said of crochets when they are arranged in a single row or series with their bases in line. (Figs. 101, 105, etc.)

Unisetose, a. Consisting of or bearing a single seta; compare bisetose.

Ventral prolegs, pl. n. Those prolegs ordinarily borne on segments 3, 4, 5, and 6; opposed to anal prolegs; hookless prolegs are sometimes also borne on segments 2 and 7 and these are also known as ventral.

Verricule, n. A dense tuft of upright setae, modified from a verruca or scolus.   (Fig. 91.)

Verruca, n. A definitely bounded, somewhat elevated portion of the cuticle, bearing several to many setae.   (Fig. 88.)

Vertical triangle, n. The thinly chitinized dorsal area bounded laterad by the caudal projections of the head capsule and caudad by the prothorax.   (Fig. 72.)

BIBLIOGRAPHY

The following list includes only those papers to which reference has
been made on preceding pages:.

BEUTENMULLER, WM.
    Monograph of the Sesiidae of North America North of Mexico. Mem.
        Am. Mus. N. H., 1, pt. vi, 1900, 217.

BUSCK, AUGUST.
    Notes on Microlepidoptera, with descriptions of New North American Spe-
        cies. Proc. Ent. Soc. Wash., 11, 1909, 87.
    On the Classification of the Microlepidoptera. do. 16, 1914, 46-54.

CHAPMAN, T. A.
    The Classification of Gracilaria and Allied Genera. Entomologist, 35, 1902,
        pp. 81, 138, 159.

DYAR, HARRISON G.
    A Classification of Lepidopterous Larvae. Ann. N. Y. Acad. Sci., 8, 1894, 194.
    Additional Notes on the Classification of Lepidopterous Larvae. Trans. N.
        Y. Acad. Sci., 14, 1895, 49.
    A Classification of Lepidoptera on Larval Characters. Am. Nat., 29, 1895,
        1066.
    Life Histories of New York Slug Caterpillars.—Conclusion. Jour. N. Y.
        Ent. Soc., 8, 1899, 235.
    A Century of Larval Descriptions. Entomologists' Record, 13, 1901, 40.
    A List of North American Lepidoptera. Bul. 52, U. S. Nat. Mus., 1902.
    The Pericopid Larvae in the National Museum. Insecutor Inscitiae Men-
        struus, 2, 1914, 62.

FELT, E. P.
    The Scorpion-Flies. Rept. State Ent. N. Y., 10, 1895, 463.

FORBES, W. T. M.
    Field Tables of Lepidoptera. 1906.
    A Structural Study of Some Caterpillars. Ann. Ent. Soc. Am., 3, 1910, 94.
    A Structural Study of the Caterpillars.—II. The Sphingidae. Ann. Ent.
        Soc. Am., 4, 1911, 261.

HOFMANN, O.
    Über die Anordnung der borstentragenden Warzen bei den Raupen der
        Pterophoriden. Illus. Zeitschr. Ent., 3, 1898, 129.

MÜLLER, WILHELM.
    Südamerikanischer Nymphalidenraupen. Zool. Jahrb., Zeitschr. f. Syst., 1,
        1886, 417.

PACKARD, A. S.
    Monograph of the Bombycine Moths. Part I. Notodontidae. Mem. Nat.
        Acad. Sci., Vol. 7, 1895.

QUAIL, AMBROSE.
    Notes on Cossidae. Entomologist, 37, 1904, 93.
    On the Tubercles of Thorax and Abdomen in First Larval Stage of Lepi-
        doptera. Ibid., p. 269.

REAUMUR.
   Mémoirés pour servir à l'histoire des Insectes.   1736-42.
SCUDDER, S. H.
   The Butterflies of the Eastern United States and Canada.   1889.
SILTALA, A. J.
   Trichopterologische Untersuchungen.   No. 2.   Zool. Jahrb., Suppl. 9, 1907,
      pp. 309-626, esp., pp. 356-375.
SPULER, ARNOLD.
   Die Schmetterlinge Europas.   Bd. 1, 1908, p. ix.
TSOU, Y. H.
   The Body Setae of Lepidopterous Larvae.   Trans. Am. Micr. Soc., 33, 1914,
      223-260. This paper was written simultaneously with the one presented here-
      with.   The results agree in the main as each was cognizant of the other's
      work.
WALSINGHAM, Lord.
   Biologia Centrali-Americana.   Lepidoptera Heterocera.   Vol. 4, incomplete,
      1911—.
WOOD, J. H.
   Notes on Earlier Stages of the Nepticulae.   Ent. Monthly Mag. (2), 5, 1894,
      pp. 1, 43, 93, 150, 272.

EXPLANATION OF PLATES

Plates I to VII and X consist entirely of setal maps. In these the top line of the diagram represents the dorsomeson and the bottom line the ventromeson. Thus the map shows the entire left half of the segment, the thoracic leg or the proleg, as the case may be, being indicated by an ellipse.

The body segments are numbered I, II, III, 1, 2, 3, 4, 5, 6, 7, 8, 9, and 10, the Roman numerals referring to the thorax and the Arabic to the abdomen. Care should be taken in using this in connection with the statements of other authors. For example, the head is counted as "joint 1", the prothorax as "joint 2", etc., in Dyar's descriptions. Dyar has also entirely failed to note segment 9 and thus, while segment 8 is his "joint 12", the anal segments is called "joint 13". In the setal maps the number of each segment is given in the lower left hand corner.

In all the figures, both of setal maps and other structures, the head is at the left.

The following is a list of all the setae. Each is indicated by a lower case Greek letter:

α alpha	θ theta	ρ rho
β beta	κ kappa	σ sigma
γ gamma	λ lambda (rare)	τ tau
δ delta	μ mu	ϕ phi
ϵ epsilon	ν nu	ω omega
η eta	π pi	

Certain definite groups of setae are indicated by capital Greek letters. They are: Beta, B $(\alpha+\beta)$; Kappa, K $(\theta+\kappa+\eta)$ Rho, P $(\epsilon+\rho)$; Pi, Π $(\nu+\pi$ on thorax, $\nu+\pi+\tau$ on abdomen); Tau, T, some or all of the three setae, tau, phi, and omega, the first of which is, however, more closely associated with the Pi group on abdominal segments. Of the Kappa group, theta is usually absent.

The ocelli are numbered as in Fig. 70.

The numerals applied to the head setae are taken direct from Forbes (1910), who uses Dyar's system for them. In his paper will be found large numbers of drawings of head parts, and for that reason only a few have been figured here.

PLATE I—II

EXPLANATION OF PLATE I

SETAL MAPS. See page 147

Fig. 1.   Hypothetical type showing the twelve primary setae. In addition three of the more usual subprimaries are dotted in. The spiracle is shown in both the prothoracic (a) and abdominal (b) positions.

Figs. 2, 3, 4.   *Hepialus mustelinus,* Hepialidae, Jugatae. Prothorax, mesothorax, and third abdominal segment, first instar. Adapted from figures by Dyar (1895b).

Fig. 5.   *Hepialus humuli.* Prothorax and mesothorax of mature larva.

Fig. 6.   *Hepialus humuli.* Abdominal segments 1 to 3 of mature larva.

Fig. 7.   *Pseudanaphora arcanella,* Acrolophidae, Tineoida. Prothorax and mesothorax of mature larva.

Fig. 8.   *Pseudanaphora arcanella.* Abdominal segments 1 to 3 of mature larva.

EXPLANATION OF PLATE II

SETAL MAPS.

Fig. 9.   Typical mesothorax of Frenatae, labeled with Greek letters.

Fig. 10.   Typical proleg-bearing abdominal segment of Frenatae, labeled with Greek letters.

Fib. 11.   Typical mesothorax of Frenatae, labeled according to Dyar's system.

Fig. 12.   Typical proleg-bearing abdominal segment of Frenatae, labeled according to Dyar's system.

Figs. 13, 14.   *Hepialus humuli,* Hepialidae. Abdominal segments 6 to 10 of mature larva. (Tau and omega are transposed in Fig. 14.)

Figs. 15, 16.   *Pseudanaphora arcanella,* Acrolophidae. Abdominal segments 6 to 10 of mature larva.

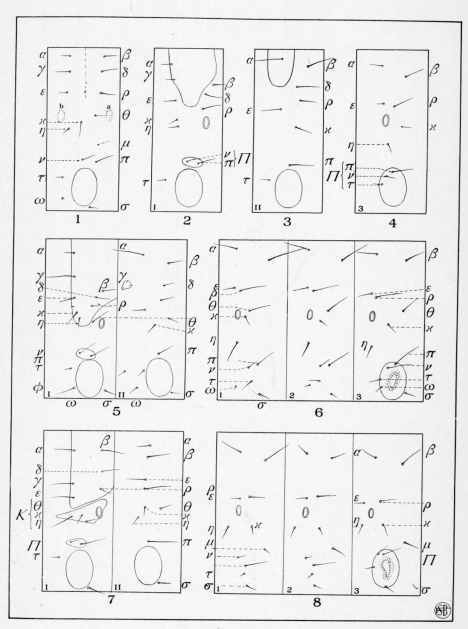

PLATE I

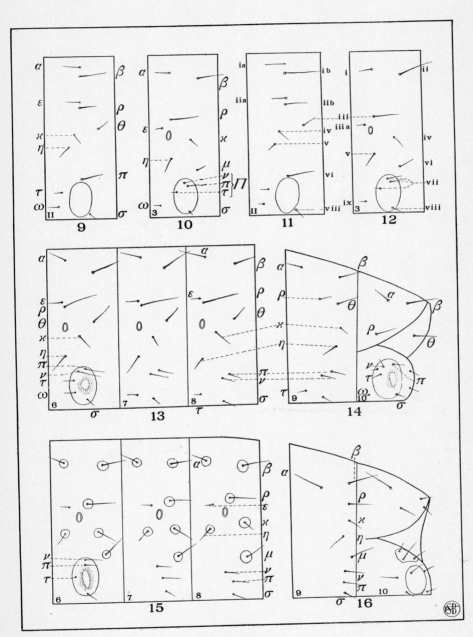

PLATE II

PLATES III—IV

EXPLANATION OF PLATE III

Setal Maps.

Figs. 17, 18, 19, 20. *Feltia gladiaria,* Noctuidae. Prothorax, mesothorax, and first and second abdominal segments respectively; first instar.

Figs. 21, 22, 23, 24. *Feltia gladiaria,* Noctuidae. Same segments of the mature larva.

Figs. 25, 26, 27, 28. *Hyphantria cunea,* Arctiidae. Same segments of the mature larva.

EXPLANATION OF PLATE IV

Setal Maps.

Figs. 29, 30. *Feltia gladiaria,* Noctuidae. Abdominal segments 6 to 10 respectively; first instar.

Figs. 31, 32. *Feltia gladiaria,* Noctuidae. Abdominal segments 6 to 10 respectively; mature larva.

Figs. 33, 34. *Hyphantria cunea,* Arctiidae. Abdominal segments 6 to 10 respectively; mature larva.

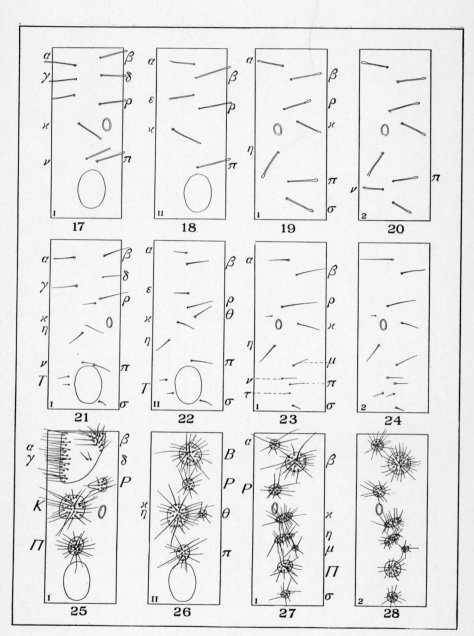

PLATE III

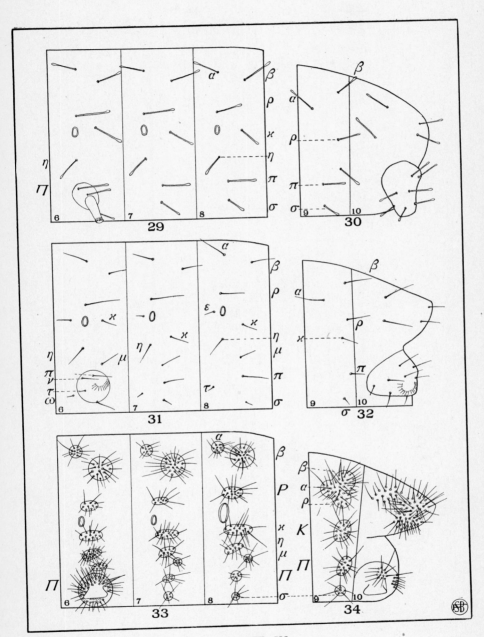

PLATE IV

PLATE V

EXPLANATION OF PLATE

S<small>ETAL</small> M<small>APS</small>.

Figs. 35, 36, 37, 38. *Atteva aurea,* Yponomeutidae. Prothorax, mesothorax, fourth
and ninth abdominal segments respectively.

Figs. 39, 40, 41, 42. *Cydia pomonella,* Tortricidae. Same segments.

Figs. 43, 44, 45, 46. *Psorosina (Canarsia) hammondi,* Phycitinae, Pyralididae.
Same segments.

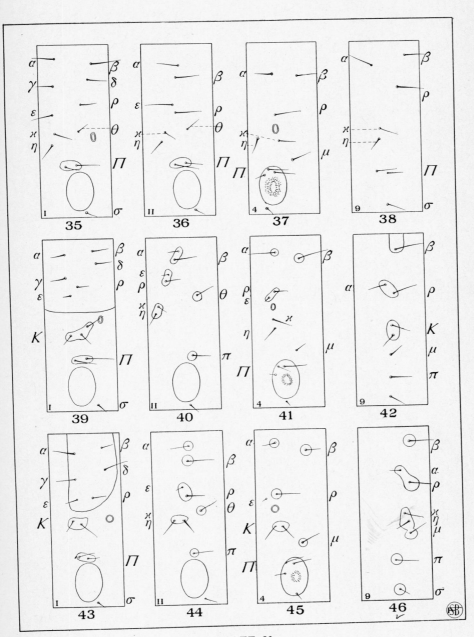

PLATE V

PLATE VI

EXPLANATION OF PLATE

SETAL MAPS.

Fig. 47.   Phycitinae, Pyralididae.   Prothorax of an unidentified species showing arrangement of setae similar to that of Melitara.

Figs. 48, 49.   *Loxostege similalis,* Pyraustinae, Pyralididae.   Third and ninth abdominal segments respectively.

Fig. 50.   *Galleria mellonella,* Galleriinae, Pyralididae.   Mesothorax.

Figs. 51, 52, 53, 54.   *Scardia fiskeella,* Tineidae.   Prothorax, mesothorax, third and ninth abdominal segments respectively.

Fig. 55.   *Thyris fenestrella,* Thyrididae.   Ninth abdominal segment.

Fig. 56.   *Gelechia* sp., Gelechiidae.   Ninth abdominal segment.

Fig. 57.   *Sanninoidea exitiosa,* Aegeriidae.   Ninth abdominal segment.

Fig. 58.   *Thyridopteryx ephemeraeformis,* Psychidae.   Third abdominal segment.

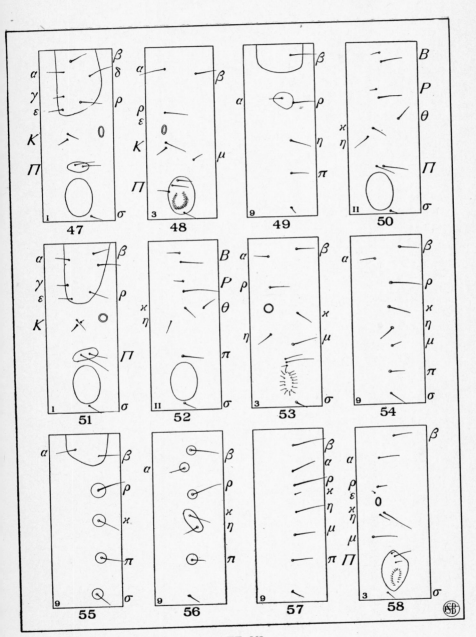

PLATE VI

PLATE VII

EXPLANATION OF PLATE

SETAL MAPS OF ABDOMINAL SEGMENTS.

Fig. 59.   *Acoloithus falsarius,* Pyromorphidae.   Segment 5.
Fig. 60.   *Nola cristatula,* Nolidae.   Segment 5.
Fig. 61.   *Oxyptilus delavaricus,* Pterophoridae.   Segment 5.
Fig. 62.   *Callizzia inornata,* Epiplemidae.   Segment 5.
Fig. 63.   *Cleora pampinaria,* Geometridae.   Segments 5, 6, 7.
Fig. 64.   *Thyatira batis,* of Europe, Thyatiridae.   Segment 4.
Figs. 65, 66.   *Acronycta* sp., Noctuidae.   Segments 6 and 7.   Note fusion of ver-
              rucae kappa and eta on segment 7.
Figs. 67, 68.   *Syntomis phegea,* of Europe, Syntomidae.   Segments 6 and 7.   Note
              that kappa is in same position on segment 7 as on segment 6.

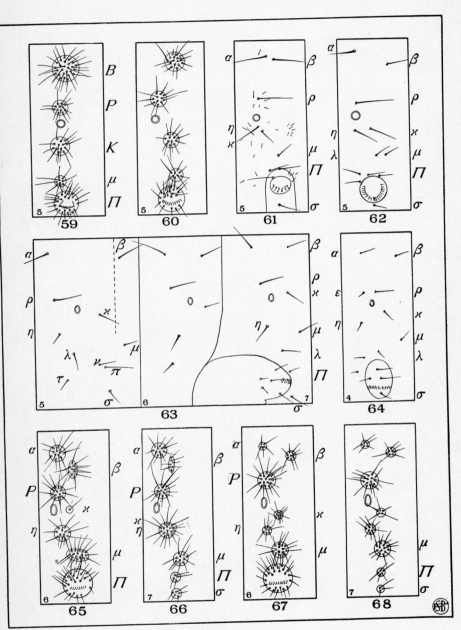

PLATE VII

PLATE VIII

EXPLANATION OF PLATE

Fig. 69. *Thyridopteryx ephemeraeformis*, Psychidae. Showing portion of prothorax which bears peculiar horizontal spiracle.

Fig. 70. *Acrobasis betulella*, Pyralididae. Ocellar group.

Fig. 71. *Plodia interpunctella*, Pyralididae. Ocellar group.

Fig. 72. *Zeuzera pyrina*, Cossidae. Head, cephalodorsal aspect, showing the very large mandibles.

Fig. 73. *Euptoieta claudia*, Nymphalidae. Subdorsal scolus of third abdominal segment.

Fig. 74. *Polygonia interrogationis*, Nymphalidae. Subdorsal scolus of eighth abdominal segment.

Fig. 75. Ocellar arrangement similar to that of *Podosesia*, Aegeriidae.

Fig. 76. *Eurycittarus confederata*, Psychidae. Front, adfrontals, and their setae.

Fig. 77. *Sanninoidea exitiosa*, Aegeriidae. Ocellar group.

Fig. 78. *Thyridopteryx ephemeraeformis*, Psychidae. Head. In all the head figures of the plate: fp—frontal puncture; f—frontal seta; afi—first adfrontal seta; afii—second adfrontal seta; afp—adfrontal puncture, borne on adfrontals between adfrontal setae.

Fig. 79. *Estigmene acraea*, Arctiidae. Spiracle.

Fig. 80. *Depressaria* sp., Oecophoridae. Ocellar group.

Fig. 81. *Anacampsis populella*, Gelechiidae. Ocellar group.

Fig. 82. *Oiketicus abbotii*, Psychidae. Front and adfrontals.

Fig. 83. *Solenobia walshella*, Psychidae. Front and adfrontals.

Fig. 84. Suranal plate of a European species of Agapetidae.

Fig. 85. *Thyridopteryx ephemeraeformis*, Psychidae. Proleg.

Fig. 86. *Celama triquetrana*, Nolidae. Ocellar group.

Fig. 87. *Nola apera*, Nolidae. Ocellar group.

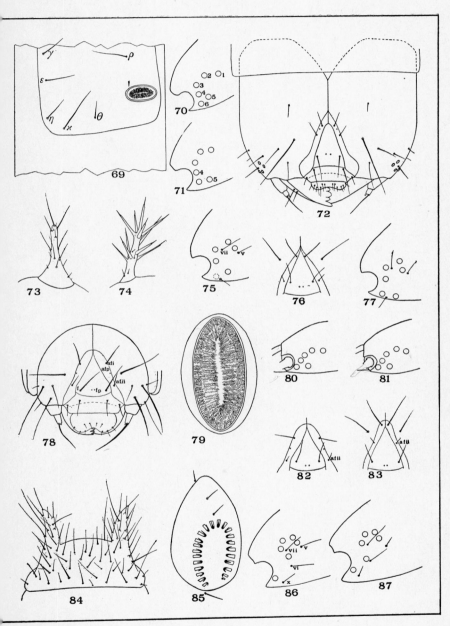

PLATE VIII

PLATE IX

EXPLANATION OF PLATE

Fig. 88.   Typical verruca of Arctiidae; *Estigmene acraea*.

Fig. 89.   *Drepana harpagula,* of Europe, Platypterygidae.   Lateral aspect showing anal process.

Fig. 90.   Typical chalaza; *Utetheisa bella,* Arctiidae.

Fig. 91.   Typical verricule; *Acronycta rubricoma.*

Fig. 92.   Typical fleshy filament; lateral aspect of *Anosia plexippus,* mesothorax.

Fig. 93.   *Nepticula* sp., Nepticulidae.   Lateral aspect of the three thoracic and first two abdominal segments showing the first three pairs of fleshy legs, and their location.

Fig. 94.   *Adela degeerella,* of Europe, Incurvariidae.   Crochets.

Fig. 95.   *Plutella maculipennis,* Yponomeutidae.   Proleg, mesal aspect.

Fig. 96.   *Pseudanaphora arcanella,* Acrolophidae.   Ventral aspect of proleg, showing crochets arranged in a multiserial circle.

Fig. 97.   *Drepana harpagula,* Platypterygidae.   Latero-ventral aspect of proleg, showing crochets arranged in a pseudocircle.

Fig. 98.   *Psorosina hammondi,* Pyraustinae, Pyralididae.   Ventral aspect of proleg, showing crochets arranged in a mesal penellipse.

Fig. 99.   *Sanninoidea exitiosa,* Aegeriidae.   Crochets arranged in transverse bands.

Fig. 100.   *Estigmene acraea,* Arctiidae.   Mesal aspect of proleg; crochets heteroideous, uniordinal, arranged in a mesoseries.

Fig. 101.   *Pyralis farinalis,* Pyralidinae, Pyralididae.   Crochets biordinal, arranged in a complete circle.

Fig. 102.   *Lycaena coridon,* Lycaenidae.   Proleg, mesal aspect, showing interrupted mesoseries and fleshy lobe.

Fig. 103.   *Ornix geminatella,* Gracilariidae.   Crochets of abdominal segment 3.

Fig. 104.   *Zygaena punctum,* Zygaenidae, of Europe.   Spiracle.

Fig. 105.   *Scolecocampa liburna,* Noctuidae.   Mesal aspect of proleg; crochets uniordinal, arranged in a mesoseries; also homoideous.

Fig. 106.   Saturniidae.   Mesal aspect of proleg; crochets biordinal, arranged in a mesoseries.

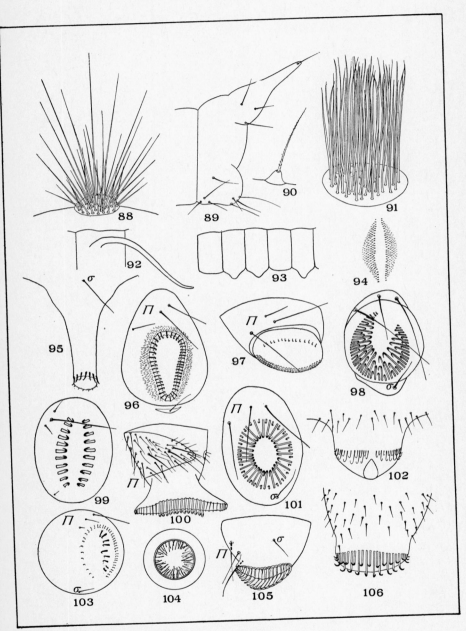

PLATE IX

PLATE X

EXPLANATION OF PLATE

Fig. 107. *Samia cecropia,* Saturniidae. Prothorax, mesothorax, and first and
         third abdominal segments.
Fig. 108. *Samia cecropia,* Saturniidae. Abdominal segments 8 and 9.
Fig. 109. *Automeris io,* Hemileucidae. Abdominal segments 8 and 9.
Fig. 110. *Citheronia regalis,* Ceratocampidae. Abdominal segments 8 and 9.
Fig. 111. *Anisota rubicunda,* Ceratocampidae. Abdominal segments 8 and 9.
Fig 112. *Polygonia interrogationis,* Nymphalidae. Abdominal segments 8 and 9.

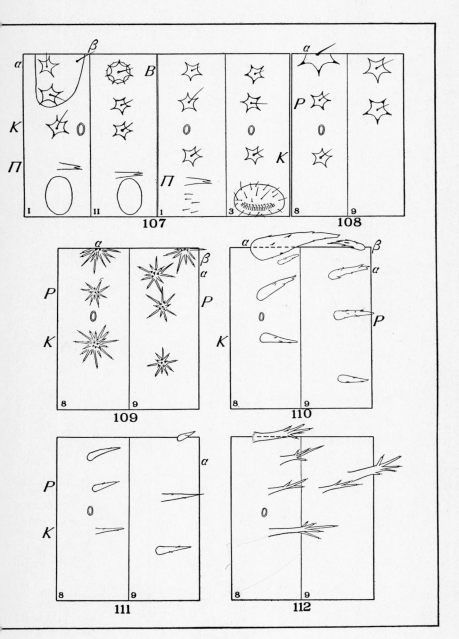

PLATE X

INDEX TO GENERA AND HIGHER GROUPS

165

INDEX

INDEX